The Sacred Beetle And Others

by

J. Henri Fabre

Double9 BOOKS

The Sacred Beetle And Others

by J. Henri Fabre

ISBN: 978-93-71817-38-7

Published by

DOUBLE 9 BOOKS

2/13-B, Ansari Road
Daryaganj, New Delhi – 110002
info@double9books.com
www.double9books.com
Tel. 011-40042856

ABOUT THE AUTHOR

Jean-Henri Casimir Fabre was a French naturalist and entomologist celebrated for his engaging writings on insect life. Born to Antoine Fabre and Victoire Salgues in Saint-Léons, France, he developed a profound interest in nature and the behaviors of insects that shaped his career. Fabre's work combined scientific observation with a lively narrative style that brought the natural world to life for readers. Throughout his life, he remained dedicated to exploring and documenting the complexities of insect behavior, particularly beetles and other small creatures. His contributions significantly influenced popular science literature and entomology, making the study of insects accessible and fascinating to a broader audience. Fabre was married twice, first to Marie-Césarine Villard and later to Marie Joséphine Daudel, and had a son named Paul-Henri Fabre. He lived a long life, passing away at the age of 91 in Sérignan-du-Comtat, France. His legacy continues through his detailed observations and writings that highlight the intricate and often overlooked aspects of insect life.

CONTENTS

AUTHOR'S PREFACE.....7

TRANSLATOR'S NOTE.....14

CHAPTER I
THE SACRED BEETLE.....15

CHAPTER II
THE SACRED BEETLE IN CAPTIVITY.....32

CHAPTER III
THE SACRED BEETLE: THE BALL.....40

CHAPTER IV
THE SACRED BEETLE: THE PEAR.....48

CHAPTER V
THE SACRED BEETLE: THE MODELLING.....58

CHAPTER VI
THE SACRED BEETLE: THE LARVA.....64

CHAPTER VII
THE SACRED BEETLE: THE NYMPH; THE RELEASE.....72

CHAPTER VII
THE BROAD-NECKED SCARAB; THE GYMNOPLEURI.....82

CHAPTER IX
THE SPANISH COPRIS: THE LAYING OF THE EGGS.....92

CHAPTER X
THE SPANISH COPRIS: THE HABITS OF THE MOTHER.....105

CHAPTER XI
ONTHOPHAGI AND ONITICELLI.....119

CHAPTER XII
THE GEOTRUPES: THE PUBLIC HEALTH.....130

CHAPTER XIII
THE GEOTRUPES: NEST-BUILDING....139

CHAPTER XIV
THE GEOTRUPES: THE LARVA....150

CHAPTER XV
THE SISYPHUS: THE INSTINCT OF PATERNITY....158

CHAPTER XVI
THE LUNARY COPRIS; THE BISON ONITIS....166

CHAPTER XVII
THE BULL ONTHOPHAGUS: THE CELL....176

CHAPTER XVIII
THE BULL ONTHOPHAGUS: THE LARVA; THE NYMPH....187

INDEX....195

AUTHOR'S PREFACE

In the building of the nest, the family safeguard, we see the highest manifestation of the faculties of instinct. That clever architect, the bird, teaches us as much; and the insect, with its still more diverse talents, repeats the lesson, telling us that maternity is the supreme inspirer of instinct. Entrusted with the preservation of the species, which is of more importance than the preservation of individuals, maternity awakens in the drowsiest intelligence marvellous gleams of foresight; it is the thrice sacred hearth where are kindled those mysterious psychic fires which will suddenly burst into flame and dazzle us with their semblance of infallible reason. The more maternity asserts itself, the higher does instinct ascend.

In this respect no creatures are more deserving of our attention than the Hymenoptera, upon whom the cares of maternity devolve in their fulness. All these favourites of instinct prepare board and lodging for their offspring. They become master-craftsmen in a host of trades for the sake of a family which their faceted eyes will never behold, but which is nevertheless no stranger to the mother's powers of foresight. One turns cotton-spinner and produces cotton-wool bottles; another sets up as a basket-maker and weaves hampers out of bits of leaves; a third becomes a mason and builds rooms of cement and domes of road-metal; a fourth opens pottery-works, where clay is kneaded into shapely vases and rounded pots; yet another goes in for mining and digs mysterious underground chambers in the warm, moist earth. A thousand trades similar to ours and often even unknown to our industrial system enter into the preparation of the abode. Next come the provisions for the expected nurselings: piles of honey, loaves of pollen, stores of game, preserved by a cunning paralysing-process. In such works as these, having the future of the family for their sole object, the highest manifestations of instinct are displayed under the stimulus of maternity.

So far as the rest of the insect race is concerned, the mother's cares are generally most summary. In the majority of cases, all that is done is to lay the eggs in a favourable spot, where the larva, at its own risk and peril, can find bed and breakfast. With such rustic ideas upon the upbringing of the offspring, talents are superfluous. Lycurgus banished the arts from his republic on the ground that they were enervating. In like manner the higher inspirations of instinct have no home among insects reared in the Spartan fashion. The mother scorns the sweet task of the nurse; and the psychic prerogatives, which are the best of all, diminish and disappear, so true is it that, with animals as with ourselves, the family is a source of perfection.

While the Hymenopteron, so extremely thoughtful of her progeny, fills us with wonder, the others, which abandon theirs to the accidents of good luck or bad, must seem to us, by comparison, of little interest. These others form almost the whole of the entomological race; at least, among the fauna of our country-sides, there is, to my knowledge, only one other example of insects preparing board and lodging for their family, as do the gatherers of honey and the buriers of well-filled game-bags.

And, strange to say, these insects vying in maternal solicitude with the flower-despoiling tribe of Bees are none other than the Dung-beetles, the dealers in ordure, the scavengers of the cattle-fouled meadows. We must pass from the scented blossoms of our flower-beds to the Mule-dung of our high-roads to find a second instance of devoted mothers and lofty instincts. Nature abounds in these antitheses. What are our ugliness or beauty, our cleanliness or dirt to her? Out of filth, she creates the flower; from a little manure, she extracts the thrice-blessed grain of wheat.

Notwithstanding their disgusting occupation, the Dung-beetles are of a very respectable standing. Their size, which is generally imposing; their severe and immaculately glossy attire; their portly bodies, thickset and compact; the quaint ornamentation of brow or thorax: all combined make them cut an excellent figure in the collector's boxes, especially when to our home species, oftenest of an ebon black, we add a few tropical varieties, a-glitter with gleams of gold and flashes of burnished copper.

They are the sedulous attendants of our herds, for which reason several of them are faintly redolent of benzoic acid, the aromatic of the Sheep-folds. Their pastoral habits have impressed the nomenclators, too often, alas, careless of euphony, who this time have changed their tune and headed their descriptions with such names as Melibœus, Tityrus, Amyntas, Corydon, Mopsus and Alexis. We find here the whole series of bucolic appellations made famous by the poets of antiquity. Virgil's eclogues have lent their vocabulary for the Dung-beetles' glorification. We should have to go back to the Butterflies with their dainty graces to find an equally poetic nomenclature. In their case the epic names of the *Iliad* ring out, borrowed from the camps of Greek and Trojan and perhaps too magnificently bellicose for those peaceable winged flowers whose habits in no wise recall the martial deeds of an Ajax or an Achilles. Much better-imagined is the bucolic title given to the Dung-beetles: it tells us the insect's chief characteristic, its predilection for pasture-lands.

The dung-manipulators have as head of their line the Sacred Beetle or Scarab, whose strange behaviour had already attracted the attention of the fellah in the valley of the Nile, some thousand years before the Christian era.

As he watered his patch of onions in the spring, the Egyptian peasant would see from time to time a fat black insect pass close by, hurriedly trundling a ball of Camel-dung backwards. He would watch the queer rolling thing in amazement, even as the Provençal peasant watches it to this day.

No one fails to be surprised when he first finds himself in the presence of the Scarab, who, with his head down and his long hind-legs in the air, pushes with might and main his huge pill, the source of so many awkward tumbles. Undoubtedly the simple fellah, on beholding this spectacle, wondered what that ball could be, what object the black creature could have in rolling it along with such vigour. The peasant of to-day asks himself the same question.

In the days of the Rameses and Thothmes, superstition had something to say in the matter; men saw in the rolling sphere an image of the world performing its daily revolution; and the Scarab received divine honours: in memory of his ancient glory, he continues the Sacred Beetle of the modern naturalists.

It is six or seven thousand years since the curious pill-maker first got himself talked about: are his habits thoroughly familiar to us yet? Do we know the exact use for which he intends his ball, do we know how he rears his family? Not at all. The most authoritative works perpetuate the grossest errors where he is concerned.

Ancient Egypt used to say that the Scarab rolls his ball from east to west, the direction in which the world turns. He next buries it underground for twenty-eight days, the period of a lunary revolution. This four weeks' incubation quickens the pill-maker's progeny. On the twenty-ninth day, which the insect knows to be that of the conjunction of the sun and moon and of the birth of the world, he goes back to his buried ball; he digs it up, opens it and throws it into the Nile. That completes the cycle. Immersion in the sacred waters causes a Scarab to emerge from the ball.

Let us not laugh overmuch at these Pharaonic stories: they contain a modicum of truth mingled with the fantastic theories of astrology. Moreover, a good deal of the laughter would recoil upon our own science, for the fundamental error of regarding as the Scarab's cradle the ball which we see rolling across the fields still lingers in our text-books. All the authors who write about the Sacred Beetle repeat it; the tradition has come down to us intact from the far-off days when the Pyramids were built.

It is a good thing from time to time to wield the hatchet in the overgrown thicket of tradition; it is well to shake off the yoke of accepted ideas. It is possible that, cleansed of its obscuring dross, truth may at last shine forth resplendent, far greater and more wonderful than the things which we were taught. I have sometimes harboured these rash doubts; and I have no reason to regret it, notably in the case of the Scarab. To-day I know the sacred pill-roller's story thoroughly; and the reader shall see how much more marvellous it is than the tales handed down to us by the old Egyptians.

The early chapters of my investigations into the nature of instinct1 have already proved, in the most categorical fashion, that the round pellets rolled hither and thither along the ground by the insect do not and indeed cannot contain germs. They are not habitations for the egg and the grub; they are provisions which the Sacred Beetle hurriedly removes from the madding crowd in order to bury them and consume them at leisure in a subterranean dining-room.

Nearly forty years have elapsed since I used eagerly to collect the materials to support my iconoclastic assertions on the Plateau des Angles, near Avignon; and nothing has happened to invalidate my statements; far from it: everything has corroborated them. The incontestable proof came at last when I obtained the Scarab's nest, a genuine nest this time, gathered in such quantities as I wished and in some cases even shaped before my eyes.

I have described my former vain attempts to find the larva's abode; I have described the pitiful failure of my efforts at rearing under cover; and perhaps the reader commiserated my woes when he saw me on the outskirts of the town stealthily and ingloriously gathering in a paper bag the donation dropped by a passing Mule for my charges. Certainly, as things were, my task was no easy one. My boarders, who were great consumers, or more correctly speaking great wasters, used to beguile the tedium of captivity by indulging in art for art's sake in the glad sunshine. Pill followed on pill, all beautifully rounded, to be abandoned unused after a few exercises in rolling. The heap of provisions, which I had so painfully acquired in the friendly shadow of the gloaming, was squandered with disheartening rapidity; and there came a time when the daily bread failed. Moreover, the stringy manna falling from the Horse and the Mule is hardly suited to the mother's work, as I learned afterwards. Something more homogeneous, more plastic is needed; and this only the Sheep's somewhat laxer bowels are able to supply.

In short, though my earlier studies taught me all about the Scarab's public manners, for several reasons they told me nothing of his private habits. The nest-building problem remained as obscure as ever. Its solution demands a good deal more than the straitened resources of a town and the scientific equipment of a laboratory. It requires prolonged residence in the country; it requires the proximity of flocks and herds in the bright sunshine. Given these conditions, success is assured, provided that one have zeal and perseverance; and these conditions I find to perfection in my quiet village.

Provisions, my great difficulty in the old days, are now to be had for the asking. Close to my house, Mules pass along the high-road, on their way to the fields and back again; morning and evening, flocks of Sheep go by, making for the pasture or the fold; not five yards from my door, my neighbour's Goat is tethered: I can hear her bleating as she nibbles away at her ring of grass. Moreover, should food be scarce in my immediate vicinity, there are always youthful purveyors who, lured by visions of lollipops, are ready to scour the country to collect victuals for my Beetles.

They arrive, not one but a dozen, bringing their contributions in the queerest of receptacles. In this novel procession of gift-bearers, any concave thing that chances to be handy is employed: the crown of an old hat, a broken tile, a bit of stove-pipe, the bottom of a spinning-top, a fragment of a basket, an old shoe hardened into a sort of boat, at a pinch the collector's own cap.

'It's prime stuff this time,' their shining eyes seem to proclaim. 'It's something extra special.'

The goods are duly approved and paid for on the spot, as agreed. To close the transaction in a fitting manner, I take the victuallers to the cages and show them the Beetle rolling his pill. They gaze in wonder at the funny creature that looks as if it were playing with its ball; they laugh at its tumbles and scream with delight at its clumsy struggles when it comes to grief and lies on its back kicking. A charming sight, especially when the lollipops bulging in the youngsters' cheeks are just beginning to melt deliciously. Thus the zeal of my little collaborators is kept alive. There is no fear of my boarders starving: their larder will be lavishly supplied.

Who are these boarders? Well, first and foremost the Sacred Beetle, the chief subject of my present investigations. Sérignan's long screen of hills might well mark his extreme northern boundary. Here ends the Mediterranean flora, whose last ligneous representatives are the arboraceous heather and the arbutus-tree; and here, in all probability, the mighty pill-maker, a passionate lover of the sun, terminates his arctic explorations. He abounds on the hot slopes facing the south and in the narrow belt of plain sheltered by that powerful reflector. According to all appearances, the elegant Gallic Bolboceras and the stalwart Spanish Copris likewise stop at this line; for both are as sensitive to cold as he. To these curious Dung-beetles, whose private habits are so little known, let us add the Gymnopleuri, the Minotaur, the Geotrupes, the Onthophagi. They are all welcomed in my cages, for all, I am convinced beforehand, have surprises in store for us in the details of their underground business.

My cages have a capacity of about a cubic yard. Except for the front, which is of wire gauze, the whole is made of wood. This keeps out any excessive rain, the effect of which would be to turn the layer of earth in my open-air appliances into mud. Over-great moisture would be fatal to the prisoners, who cannot, in their straitened artificial demesne, act as they do when at liberty and prolong their digging indefinitely until they come upon a medium suitable to their operations. They want soil which is porous and not too dry, though in no danger of ever becoming muddy. The earth in the cages therefore is of a sandy character and, after being sifted, is slightly moistened and flattened down just enough to prevent any landslips in the future galleries. Its depth is barely ten or eleven inches, which is insufficient in certain cases; but those of the inmates who have a fancy for deep galleries, like the Geotrupes for instance, are well able to make up horizontally for what is denied them perpendicularly.

The trellised front has a south aspect and allows the sun's rays to penetrate right into the dwelling. The opposite side, which faces north, consists of two shutters one above the other. They are movable and are kept in place by hooks or bolts. The top one opens for food to be distributed and for the cleaning of the cage; it is the kitchen-door for everyday use. It is also the entrance-gate for any new captives whom I succeed in bagging. The bottom shutter, which keeps the layer of earth in position, is opened only on great occasions, when we want to surprise the insect in its home life and to ascertain the condition of the progress underground. Then the bolts are drawn; the board, which is on hinges, falls; and a vertical section of the soil is laid bare, giving us an excellent opportunity of studying the Dung-beetles' work. Our examination is made with the point of a knife and has to be conducted with the utmost care. In this way we get with precision and without difficulty industrial details which could not always be obtained by laborious digging in the open fields.

Nevertheless, outdoor investigations are indispensable and often yield far more important results than anything derived from home rearing; for, though some Dung-beetles are indifferent to captivity and work in the cage with their customary vigour, others, who are of a more nervous temperament or perhaps more cautious, distrust my boarded palaces and are extremely reluctant to surrender their secrets. It is only once in a way that they fall victims to my assiduous wooing. Besides, if my menagerie is to be run properly, I must know something of what is happening outside, were it only to find out the right time of year for my various projects. It is absolutely essential therefore that our study of the insect in captivity should be amply supplemented by observations of its life and habits in the wild state.

Here an assistant would be very useful to me, some one with leisure, with a seeing eye and a simple heart, whose curiosity would be as unaffected as my own. This helper I have: such an one indeed as I have never had before or since. He is a young shepherd, a friend of the family. He has read a little and has a keen desire for knowledge, so he is not frightened by the terms Scarabæus, Geotrupes, Copris or Onthophagus when I name the insects which he has dug up the day before and kept for me in a box.

At early dawn in the dog-days, when my insects are busy with their nest-building, you may see him in the meadows. When night falls and the heat begins to lessen, he is still there; and all day long, till far into the night, he passes to and fro among the pill-rollers, who are attracted from every quarter by the reek of the victuals strewn by his Sheep. Well-posted in the various points of my entomological problems, he watches events and keeps me informed. He awaits his opportunity; he inspects the grass. With his knife he lays bare the subterranean cell which is betrayed by its little mound of earth; he scrapes, digs and finds; and it all constitutes a glorious change from his vague pastoral musings.

Ah, what splendid mornings we spend together, in the cool of the day, seeking the nest of the Scarab or the Copris! Old Sultan is there, seated on some knoll or other and keeping an autocratic eye upon the fleecy rabble. Nothing, not even the crust which a friend holds out to him, distracts his attention from his exalted functions. Certainly he is not much to look at, with his tangled black coat, soiled with the thousands of seeds which have caught in it. He is not a handsome Dog, but what a lot of sense there is in his shaggy head, what a talent for knowing exactly what is permitted and what forbidden, for perceiving the absence of some heedless one forgotten behind a dip in the ground! Upon my word, one would think that he knew the number of Sheep confided to his care, *his* Sheep, though never a bone of them comes his way! He has counted them from the top of his knoll. One is missing. Sultan rushes off. Here he comes, bringing the straggler back to the flock. Clever Dog! I admire your skill in arithmetic, though I fail to understand how your crude brain ever acquired it. Yes, old fellow, we can rely on you; the two of us, your master and I, can hunt the Dung-beetle at our ease and disappear in the copsewood; not one of your charges will go astray, not one will nibble at the neighbouring vines.

It was in this way that I worked, at early morn, before the sun grew too hot, in partnership with the young shepherd and our common friend Sultan, though at times I was alone, myself sole pastor of the seventy bleating Sheep. And so the materials were gathered for this history of the Sacred Beetle and his rivals.

1 Chapters I. and II. of the present volume, forming the first two chapters of Vol. I. of the *Souvenirs entomologiques*. The remaining chapters on the Sacred Beetle appeared, in the original, in Vol. V. of that work, for which volume the above was written as a preface.—*Translator's Note.*

TRANSLATOR'S NOTE

This is the first of the four volumes containing Fabre's essays on Beetles, the order of insects to which, if we judge by his output, he devoted the longest study. It will be followed in due course by *The Glow-worm and Other Beetles, The Life of the Weevil,* and *More Beetles*. These three, however, will be issued, not in immediate succession, but turn by turn with books upon other insects; for the *Souvenirs entomologiques,* from which all or nearly all this material is taken, are still far from being exhausted.

Of the eighteen chapters that make up the present volume, some have appeared, either complete or in a more or less abbreviated form, in various interesting illustrated miscellanies published independently of the Collected Edition. Part of the Author's Preface and the chapters entitled 'The Sacred Beetle' and 'The Sacred Beetle in Captivity' will be found in *Insect Life,* prepared for Messrs. Macmillan and Co. by the author of *Mademoiselle Mori.* Similarly, the next three chapters on the Sacred Beetle, the two treating of the Spanish Copris, the chapter on the Onthophagi and Oniticelli, and the first two chapters on the Geotrupes form part of *The Life and Love of the Insect,* translated by myself for Messrs. Adam and Charles Black and published in America by the Macmillan Co. Lastly, *The Sisyphus: the Instinct of Paternity* occurs in Mr. Fisher Unwin's *Social Life in the Insect World,* translated by Mr. Bernard Miall and published in America by the Century Co. These chapters are all included in the Collected Edition by arrangement with the publishers named.

It remains for me (I grieve to say, for the last time) to acknowledge my debt to the late Miss Frances Rodwell, my very capable assistant, who did so much to assist me in preparing this and most of the previous volumes. Her too early death, in the winter of this year, was an occasion of sorrow, and a great loss to many besides myself.

Alexander Teixeira de Mattos.

Chelsea, *26th April 1919.*

CHAPTER I
THE SACRED BEETLE

It happened like this. There were five or six of us: myself, the oldest, officially their master but even more their friend and comrade; they, lads with warm hearts and joyous imaginations, overflowing with that youthful vitality which makes us so enthusiastic and so eager for knowledge. We started off one morning down a path fringed with dwarf elder and hawthorn, whose clustering blossoms were already a paradise for the Rose-chafer ecstatically drinking in their bitter perfumes. We talked as we went. We were going to see whether the Sacred Beetle had yet made his appearance on the sandy plateau of Les Angles,1 whether he was rolling that pellet of dung in which ancient Egypt beheld an image of the world; we were going to find out whether the stream at the foot of the hill was not hiding under its mantle of duckweed young Newts with gills like tiny branches of coral; whether that pretty little fish of our rivulets, the Stickleback, had donned his wedding scarf of purple and blue; whether the newly arrived Swallow was skimming the meadows on pointed wing, chasing the Crane-flies, who scatter their eggs as they dance through the air; if the Eyed Lizard was sunning his blue-speckled body on the threshold of a burrow dug in the sandstone; if the Laughing Gull, travelling from the sea in the wake of the legions of fish that ascend the Rhone to milt in its waters, was hovering in his hundreds over the river, ever and anon uttering his cry so like a maniac's laughter; if ... but that will do. To be brief, let us say that, like good simple folk who find pleasure in all living things, we were off to spend a morning at the most wonderful of festivals, life's springtime awakening.

Our expectations were fulfilled. The Stickleback was dressed in his best: his scales would have paled the lustre of silver; his throat was flashing with the brightest vermilion. On the approach of the great black Horse-leech, the spines on his back and sides started up, as though worked by a spring. In the face of this resolute altitude, the bandit turns tail and slips ignominiously down among the water-weeds. The placid mollusc tribe—Planorbes, Limnæi and other Water-snails—were sucking in the air on the surface of the water. The Hydrophilus and her hideous larva, those pirates of the ponds, darted amongst them, wringing a neck or two as they passed. The stupid crowd did not seem even to notice it. But let us leave the plain and its waters and clamber up the bluff to the plateau above us. Up there, Sheep are grazing and Horses being exercised for the approaching races, while all are distributing manna to the enraptured Dung-beetles.

Here are the scavengers at work, the Beetles whose proud mission it is to purge the soil of its filth. One would never weary of admiring the variety of tools wherewith they are supplied, whether for shifting, cutting up and shaping the stercoral matter or for excavating deep burrows in which they will seclude themselves with their booty. This equipment resembles a technical museum where every digging-implement is represented. It includes things that seem copied from those appertaining to human industry and others of so original a type that they might well serve us as models for new inventions.

The Spanish Copris carries on his forehead a powerful pointed horn, curved backwards, like the long blade of a mattock. In addition to a similar horn, the Lunary Copris has two strong spikes, curved like a ploughshare, springing from the thorax and also, between the two, a jagged protuberance which does duty as a broad rake. *Bubas bubalis* and *B. bison*, both exclusively Mediterranean species, have their forehead armed with two stout diverging horns, between which juts a horizontal dagger, supplied by the corselet. *Minotaurus typhœus* carries on the front of his thorax three ploughshares, which stick straight out, parallel to one another, the side ones longer than the middle one. The Bull Onthophagus has as his tool two long curved pieces that remind us of the horns of a Bull; the Cow Onthophagus, on the other hand, has a two-pronged fork standing erect on his flat head. Even the poorest have, either on their head or on their corselet, hard knobs that make implements which the patient insect can turn to good use, notwithstanding their bluntness. All are supplied with a shovel, that is to say, they have a broad, flat head with a sharp edge; all use a rake, that is to say, they collect materials with their toothed fore-legs.

As some sort of compensation for their unsavoury task, several of them give out a powerful scent of musk, while their bellies shine like polished metal. The Mimic Geotrupes has gleams of copper and gold beneath; the Stercoraceous Geotrupes has a belly of amethystine violet. But generally their colouring is black. The Dung-beetles in gorgeous raiment, those veritable living gems, belong to the tropics. Upper Egypt can show us under its Camel-dung a Beetle rivalling the emerald's brilliant green; Guiana, Brazil and Senegambia boast of Copres that are a metallic red, rich as copper and ruby-bright. The Dung-beetles of our climes cannot flaunt such jewellery, but they are no less remarkable for their habits.

What excitement over a single patch of Cow-dung! Never did adventurers hurrying from the four corners of the earth display such eagerness in working a Californian claim. Before the sun becomes too hot, they are there in their hundreds, large and small, of every sort, shape and size, hastening to carve themselves a slice of the common cake. There are some that labour in the open air and scrape the surface; there are others that dig themselves galleries in the thick of the heap, in search of choice veins; some work the lower stratum and bury their spoil without delay in the ground just below; others again, the smallest, keep on one side and crumble a morsel that has slipped their way during the mighty excavations of their more powerful fellows. Some, newcomers and doubtless the hungriest, consume their meal on the spot; but the greater number dream of accumulating stocks that will allow them to spend long days in affluence, down in some safe retreat. A nice, fresh patch of dung is not found just when you want it, in the barren plains overgrown with thyme; a windfall of this sort is as manna from the sky; only fortune's favourites receive so fair a portion. Wherefore the riches of to-day are prudently hoarded for the morrow. The stercoraceous scent has carried the glad tidings half a mile around; and all have hastened up to get a store of provisions. A few laggards are still arriving, on the wing or on foot.

Who is this that comes trotting towards the heap, fearing lest he reach it too late? His long legs move with awkward jerks, as though driven by some mechanism within his belly; his little red antennæ unfurl their fan, a sign of anxious greed. He is coming, he has come, not without sending a few banqueters sprawling. It is the Sacred Beetle, clad all in black, the biggest and most famous of our Dung-beetles. Behold him at table, beside his fellow-guests, each of whom is giving the last touches to his ball with the flat of his broad fore-legs or else enriching it with yet one more layer before retiring to enjoy the fruit of his labours in peace. Let us follow the construction of the famous ball in all its phases.

The clypeus, or shield, that is the edge of the broad, flat head, is notched with six angular teeth arranged in a semicircle. This constitutes the tool for digging and cutting up, the rake that lifts and casts aside the unnutritious vegetable fibres, goes for something better, scrapes and collects it. A choice is thus made, for these connoisseurs differentiate between one thing and another, making a rough selection when the Beetle is occupied with his own provender, but an extremely scrupulous one when it is a matter of constructing the maternal ball, which has a central cavity in which the egg will hatch. Then every scrap of fibre is conscientiously rejected and only the stercoral quintessence is gathered as the material for building the inner layer of the cell. The young larva, on issuing from the egg, thus finds in the very walls of its lodging a food of special delicacy which strengthens its digestion and enables it afterwards to attack the coarse outer layers.

Where his own needs are concerned, the Beetle is less particular and contents himself with a very general sorting. The notched shield then does its scooping and digging, its casting aside and scraping together more or less at random. The fore-legs play a mighty part in the work. They are flat, bow-shaped, supplied with powerful nervures and armed on the outside with five strong teeth. If a vigorous effort be needed to remove an obstacle or to force a way through the thickest part of the heap, the Dung-beetle makes use of his elbows, that is to say, he flings his toothed legs to right and left and clears a semicircular space with an energetic sweep. Room once made, a different kind of work is found for these same limbs: they collect armfuls of the stuff raked together by the shield and push it under the insect's belly, between the four hinder legs. These are formed for the turner's trade. They are long and slender, especially the last pair, slightly bowed and finished with a very sharp claw. They are at once recognised as compasses, capable of embracing a globular body in their curved branches and of verifying and correcting its shape. Their function is, in fact, to fashion the ball.

Armful by armful, the material is heaped up under the belly, between the four legs, which, by a slight pressure, impart their own curve to it and give it a preliminary outline. Then, every now and again, the rough-hewn pill is set spinning between the four branches of the double pair of spherical compasses; it turns under the Dung-beetle's belly until it is rolled into a perfect ball. Should the surface layer lack plasticity and threaten to peel off, should some too-stringy part refuse to yield to the action of the lathe, the fore-legs touch up the faulty places; their broad paddles pat the ball to give consistency to the new layer and to work the recalcitrant bits into the mass.

Under a hot sun, when time presses, one stands amazed at the turner's feverish activity. And so the work proceeds apace: what a moment ago was a tiny pellet is now a ball the size of a walnut; soon it will be the size of an apple. I have seen some gluttons manufacture a ball the size of a man's fist. This indeed means food in the larder for days to come!

The Beetle has his provisions. The next thing is to withdraw from the fray and transport the victuals to a suitable place. Here the Scarab's most striking characteristics begin to show themselves. Straightway he begins his journey; he clasps his sphere with his two long hind-legs, whose terminal claws, planted in the mass, serve as pivots; he obtains a purchase with the middle pair of legs; and, with his toothed fore-arms, pressing in turn upon the ground, to do duty as levers, he proceeds with his load, he himself moving backwards, body bent, head down and hind-quarters in the air. The rear legs, the principal factor in the mechanism, are in continual movement backwards and forwards, shifting the claws to change the axis of rotation, to keep the load balanced and to push it along by alternate thrusts to right and left. In this way the ball finds itself touching the ground by turns with every point of its surface, a process which perfects its shape and gives an even consistency to its outer layer by means of pressure uniformly distributed.

And now to work with a will! The thing moves, it begins to roll; we shall get there, though not without difficulty. Here is a first awkward place: the Beetle is wending his way athwart a slope and the heavy mass tends to follow the incline; the insect, however, for reasons best known to itself, prefers to cut across this natural road, a bold project which may be brought to naught by a false step or by a grain of sand that disturbs the balance of the load. The false step is made: down goes the ball to the bottom of the valley; and the insect, toppled over by the shock, is lying on its back, kicking. It is soon up again and hastens to harness itself once more to its load. The machine works better than ever. But look out, you dunderhead! Follow the dip of the valley: that will save labour and mishaps; the road is good and level; your ball will roll quite easily. Not a bit of it! The Beetle prepares once again to mount the slope that has already been his undoing. Perhaps it suits him to return to the heights. Against that I have nothing to say: the Scarab's judgment is better than mine as to the advisability of keeping to lofty regions; he can see farther than I can in these matters. But at least take this path, which will lead you up by a gentle incline! Certainly not! Let him find himself near some very steep slope, impossible to climb, and that is the very path which the obstinate fellow will choose. Now begins a Sisyphean labour. The ball, that enormous burden, is painfully hoisted, step by step, with infinite precautions, to a certain height, always backwards. We wonder by what miracle of statics a mass of this size can be kept upon the slope. Oh! An ill-advised movement frustrates all this toil: the ball rolls down, dragging the Beetle with it. Once more the heights are scaled and another fall is the sequel. The attempt is renewed, with greater skill this time at the difficult points; a wretched grass-root, the cause of the previous falls, is carefully got over. We are almost there; but steady now, steady! It is a dangerous ascent and the merest trifle may yet ruin everything. For see, a leg slips on a smooth bit of gravel! Down come ball and Beetle, all mixed up together. And the insect begins over again, with indefatigable obstinacy. Ten times, twenty times, he will attempt the hopeless ascent, until his persistence vanquishes all obstacles, or until, wisely recognizing the futility of his efforts, he adopts the level road.

The Scarab does not always push his precious ball alone: sometimes he takes a partner; or, to be accurate, the partner takes him. This is the way in which things usually happen: once his ball is ready, a Dung-beetle issues from the crowd and leaves the workyard, pushing his prize backwards. A neighbour, a newcomer, whose own task is hardly begun, abruptly drops his work and runs to the moving ball, to lend a hand to the lucky owner, who seems to accept the proffered aid kindly. Henceforth the two work in partnership. Each does his best to push the pellet to a place of safety. Was a compact really concluded in the workyard, a tacit agreement to share the cake between them? While one was kneading and moulding the ball, was the other tapping rich veins whence to extract choice materials and add them to the common store? I have never observed any such collaboration; I have always seen each Dung-beetle occupied solely with his own affairs in the works. The last-comer, therefore, has no acquired rights.

Can it then be a partnership between the two sexes, a couple intending to set up house? I thought so for a time. The two Beetles, one before, one behind, pushing the heavy ball with equal fervour, reminded me of a song which the hurdy-gurdies used to grind out some years ago:

> *Pour monter notre ménage, hélas! comment ferons-nous?*
> *Toi devant et moi derrière, nous pousserons le tonneau.* 2

The evidence of the scalpel compelled me to abandon my belief in this domestic idyll. There is no outward difference between the two sexes in the Scarabæi. I therefore dissected the pair of Dung-beetles engaged in trundling one and the same ball; and they very often proved to be of the same sex.

Neither community of family nor community of labour! Then what is the motive for this apparent partnership? It is purely and simply an attempt at robbery. The zealous fellow-worker, on the false plea of lending a helping hand, cherishes a plan to purloin the ball at the first opportunity. To make one's own ball at the heap means hard work and patience; to steal one ready-made, or at least to foist one's self as a guest, is a much easier matter. Should the owner's vigilance slacken, you can run away with his property; should you be too closely watched, you can sit down to table uninvited, pleading services rendered. It is 'Heads I win, tails you lose' in these tactics, so that pillage is practised as one of the most lucrative of trades. Some go to work craftily, in the way which I have described: they come to the aid of a comrade who has not the least need of them and hide the most barefaced greed under the cloak of charitable assistance. Others, bolder perhaps, more confident in their strength, go straight to their goal and commit robbery with violence.

Scenes are constantly happening such as this: a Scarab goes off, peacefully, by himself, rolling his ball, his lawful property, acquired by conscientious work. Another comes flying up, I know not whence, drops down heavily, folds his dingy wings under their cases and, with the back of his toothed fore-arms, knocks over the owner, who is powerless to ward off the attack in his awkward position, harnessed as he is to his property. While the victim struggles to his feet, the other perches himself atop the ball, the best position from which to repel an assailant. With his fore-arms crossed over his breast, ready to hit back, he awaits events. The dispossessed one moves round the ball, seeking a favourable spot at which to make the assault; the usurper spins round on the roof of the citadel, facing his opponent all the time. If the latter raise himself in order to scale the wall, the robber gives him a blow that stretches him on his back. Safe at the top of his fortress, the besieged Beetle could foil his adversary's attempts indefinitely if the latter did not change his tactics. He turns sapper so as to reduce the citadel with the garrison. The ball, shaken from below, totters and begins rolling, carrying with it the thieving Dung-beetle, who makes violent efforts to maintain his position on the top. This he succeeds in doing—though not invariably—thanks to hurried gymnastic feats which land him higher on the ball and make up for the ground which he loses by its rotation. Should a false movement bring him to earth, the chances become equal and the struggle turns into a wrestling-match. Robber and robbed grapple with each other, breast to breast. Their legs lock and unlock, their joints intertwine, their horny armour clashes and grates with the rasping sound of metal under the file. Then the one who succeeds in throwing his opponent and releasing himself scrambles to the top of the ball and there takes up his position. The siege is renewed, now by the robber, now by the robbed, as the chances of the hand-to-hand conflict may decree. The former, a brawny desperado, no novice at the game, often has the best of the fight. Then, after two or three unsuccessful attempts, the defeated Beetle wearies and returns philosophically to the heap, to make himself a new pellet. As for the other, with all fear of a surprise attack at an end, he harnesses himself to the conquered ball and pushes it whither he pleases. I have sometimes seen a third thief appear upon the scene and rob the robber. Nor can I honestly say that I was sorry.

I ask myself in vain what Proudhon3 introduced into Scarabæan morality the daring paradox that 'property means plunder,' or what diplomatist taught the Dung-beetle the savage maxim that 'might is right.' I have no data that would enable me to trace the origin of these spoliations, which have become a custom, of this abuse of strength to capture a lump of ordure. All that I can say is that theft is a general practice among the Scarabs. These dung-rollers rob one another with a calm effrontery which, to my knowledge, is without a parallel. I leave it to future observers to elucidate this curious problem in animal psychology and I go back to the two partners rolling their ball in concert.

But first let me dispel a current error in the text-books. I find in M. Émile Blanchard's4 magnificent work, *Métamorphoses, mœurs et instincts des insectes,* the following passage:

> 'Sometimes our insect is stopped by an insurmountable obstacle; the ball has fallen into a hole. At such moments the Ateuchus5 gives evidence of a really astonishing grasp of the situation as well as of a system of ready communication between individuals of the same

species which is even more remarkable. Recognizing the impossibility of coaxing the ball out of the hole, the Ateuchus seems to abandon it and flies away. If you are sufficiently endowed with that great and noble virtue called patience, stay by the forsaken ball: after a while, the Ateuchus will return to the same spot and will not return alone; he will be accompanied by two, three, four or five companions, who will all alight at the place indicated and will combine their efforts to raise the load. The Ateuchus has been to fetch reinforcements; and this explains why it is such a common sight, in the dry fields, to see several Ateuchi joining in the removal of a single ball.'

Lastly, I read in Illiger's6 *Entomological Magazine*:

> 'A *Gymnopleurus pilularius*,7 while constructing the ball of dung destined to contain her eggs, let it roll into a hole, whence she strove for a long time to extract it unaided. Finding that she was wasting her time in vain efforts, she ran to a neighbouring heap of manure to fetch three individuals of her own species, who, uniting their strength to hers, succeeded in withdrawing the ball from the cavity into which it had fallen and then returned to their manure to continue their work.'

I crave a thousand pardons of my illustrious master, M. Blanchard, but things certainly do not happen as he says. To begin with, the two accounts are so much alike that they must have had a common origin. Illiger, on the strength of observations not continuous enough to deserve blind confidence, put forward the case of his Gymnopleurus; and the same story was repeated about the Scarabæi because it is, in fact, quite usual to see two of these insects occupied together either in rolling a ball or in getting it out of a troublesome place. But this cooperation in no way proves that the Dung-beetle who found himself in difficulties went to requisition the aid of his mates. I have had no small measure of the patience recommended by M. Blanchard; I have lived laborious days in close intimacy, if I may say so, with the Sacred Beetle; I have done everything that I could think of in order to enter as thoroughly as possible into his ways and habits and to study them from life; and I have never seen anything that suggested either nearly or remotely the idea of companions summoned to lend assistance. As I shall presently relate, I have subjected the Dung-beetle to far more serious trials than that of getting his ball into a hole; I have confronted him with much graver difficulties than that of mounting a slope, which is sheer sport to the obstinate Sisyphus, who seems to delight in the rough gymnastics involved in climbing steep places, as if the ball thereby grew firmer and accordingly increased in value; I have created artificial situations in which the insect had the uttermost need of help; and never did my eyes detect any evidence of friendly services rendered by comrade to comrade. I have seen Beetles robbed and Beetles robbing and nothing more. If a number of them were gathered around the same pill, it meant that a battle was taking place. My humble opinion, therefore, is that the incident of a number of Scarabæi collected around the same ball with thieving intentions has given rise to these stories of comrades called in to lend a hand. Imperfect observations are responsible for this transformation of the bold highwayman into a helpful companion who has left his work to do another a friendly turn.

It is no light matter to attribute to an insect a really astonishing grasp of a situation, combined with an even more amazing power of communication between individuals of the same species. Such an admission involves more than one imagines. That is why I insist on my point. What! Are we to believe that a Beetle in distress will conceive the idea of going in quest of help? We are to imagine him flying off and scouring the country to find fellow-workers on some patch of dung; when he has found them, we are to suppose that he addresses them, in a sort of pantomime, by gestures with his antennæ more particularly, in some such words as these:

'I say, you fellows, my load's upset in a hole over there; come and help me get it out. I'll do as much for you one day!'

And we are to believe that his comrades understand! And, more incredible still, that they straightway leave their work, the pellet which they have just begun, the beloved pill exposed to the cupidity of others and certain to be filched in their absence, and go to the help of the suppliant! I am profoundly incredulous of such unselfishness; and my incredulity is confirmed by what I have witnessed for years and years, not in glass-cases but in the very places where the Scarab works. Apart from its maternal solicitude, in which respect it is nearly always admirable, the insect cares for nothing but itself, unless it lives in societies, like the Hive-bees, the Ants and the rest.

But let me end this digression, which is excused by the importance of the subject. I was saying that a Sacred Beetle, in possession of a ball which he is pushing backwards, is often joined by another, who comes hurrying up to lend an assistance which is anything but disinterested, his intention being to rob his companion if the opportunity present itself. Let us call the two workers partners, though that is not the proper name for them, seeing that the one forces himself upon the other, who probably accepts outside help only for fear of a worse evil. The meeting, by the way, is absolutely peaceful. The owner of the ball does not cease work for an instant on the arrival of the newcomer; and his uninvited assistant seems animated by the best intentions and sets to work on the spot. The way in which the two partners harness themselves differs. The proprietor occupies the chief position, the place of honour: he pushes at the rear, with his hind-legs in the air and his head down. His subordinate is in front, in the reverse posture, head up, toothed arms on the ball, long hind-legs on the ground. Between the two, the ball rolls along, one driving it before him, the other pulling it towards him.

The efforts of the couple are not always very harmonious, the more so as the assistant has his back to the road to be traversed, while the owner's view is impeded by the load. The result is that they are constantly having accidents, absurd tumbles, taken cheerfully and in good part: each picks himself up quickly and resumes the same position as before. On level ground this system of traction does not correspond with the dynamic force expended, through lack of precision in the combined movements: the Scarab at the back would do as well and better if left to himself. And so the helper, having given a proof of his good-will at the risk of throwing the machinery out of gear, now decides to keep still, without letting go of the precious ball, of course. He already looks upon that as his: a ball touched is a ball gained. He won't be so silly as not to stick to it: the other might give him the slip!

So he gathers his legs flat under his belly, encrusting himself, so to speak, on the ball and becoming one with it. Henceforth, the whole concern—the ball and the Beetle clinging to its surface—is rolled along by the efforts of the lawful owner. The intruder sits tight and lies low, heedless whether the load pass over his body, whether he be at the top, bottom or side of the rolling ball. A queer sort of assistant, who gets a free ride so as to make sure of his share of the victuals!

But a steep ascent heaves in sight and gives him a fine part to play. He takes the lead now, holding up the heavy mass with his toothed arms, while his mate seeks a purchase in order to hoist the load a little higher. In this way, by a combination of well-directed efforts, the Beetle above gripping, the one below pushing, I have seen a couple mount hills which would have been too much for a single carter, however persevering. But in times of difficulty not all show the same zeal: there are some who, on awkward slopes where their assistance is most needed, seem blissfully unaware of the trouble. While the unhappy Sisyphus exhausts himself in attempts to get over the bad part, the other quietly leaves him to it: imbedded in the ball, he rolls down with it if it comes to grief and is hoisted up with it when they start afresh.

I have often tried the following experiment on the two partners in order to judge their inventive faculties when placed in a serious predicament. Suppose them to be on level ground, number two seated motionless on the ball, number one busy pushing. Without disturbing the latter, I nail the ball to the ground with a long, strong pin. It stops suddenly. The Beetle, unaware of my perfidy, doubtless believes that some natural obstacle, a rut, a tuft of couch-grass, a pebble, bars the way. He redoubles his efforts, struggles his hardest; nothing happens.

'What can the matter be? Let's go and see.'

The Beetle walks two or three times round his pellet. Discovering nothing to account for its immobility, he returns to the rear and starts pushing again. The ball remains stationary.

'Let's look up above.'

The Beetle goes up, to find nothing but his motionless colleague, for I had taken care to drive in the pin so deep that the head disappeared in the ball. He explores the whole upper surface and comes down again. Fresh thrusts are vigorously applied in front and at the sides, with the same absence of success. There is not a doubt about it: never before was Dung-beetle confronted with such a problem in inertia.

Now is the time, the very time, to claim assistance, which is all the easier as his mate is there, close at hand, squatting on the summit of the ball. Will the Scarab rouse him? Will he talk to him like this:

'What are you doing there, lazybones? Come and look at the thing: it's broken down!'

Nothing proves that he does anything of the kind, for I see him steadily shaking the unshakable, inspecting his stationary machine on every side, while all this time his companion sits resting. At long last, however, the latter becomes aware that something unusual is happening; he is apprised of it by his mate's restless tramping and by the immobility of the ball. He comes down, therefore, and in his turn examines the machine. Double harness does no better than single harness. This is beginning to look serious. The little fans of the Beetles' antennæ open and shut, open again, betraying by their agitation acute anxiety. Then a stroke of genius ends the perplexity:

'Who knows what's underneath?'

They now start exploring below the ball; and a little digging soon reveals the presence of the pin. They recognize at once that the trouble is there.

If I had had a voice in their deliberations, I should have said:

'We must make a hole in the ball and pull out that skewer which is holding it down.'

This most elementary of all proceedings and one so easy to such expert diggers was not adopted, was not even tried. The Dung-beetle was shrewder than man. The two colleagues, one on this side, one on that, slip under the ball, which begins to slide up the pin, getting higher and higher in proportion as the living wedges make their way underneath. The clever operation is made possible by the softness of the material, which gives easily and makes a channel under the head of the immovable stake. Soon the pellet is suspended at a height equal to the thickness of the Scarabs' bodies. The rest is not such plain sailing. The Dung-beetles, who at first were lying flat, rise gradually to their feet, still pushing with their backs. The work becomes harder and harder as the legs, in straightening out, lose their strength; but none the less they do it. Then comes a time when they can no longer push with their backs, the limit of their height having been reached. A last resource remains, but one much less favourable to the development of motive power. This is for the insect to adopt one or other of its postures when harnessed to the ball, head down or up, and to push with its hind- or fore-legs, as the case may be. Finally the ball drops to the ground, unless we have used too long a pin. The gash made by our stake is repaired, more or less, and the carting of the precious pellet is at once resumed.

But, should the pin really be too long, then the ball, which remains firmly fixed, ends by being suspended at a height above that of the insect's full stature. In that case, after vain evolutions around the unconquerable greased pole, the Dung-beetles throw up the sponge, unless we are sufficiently kind-hearted to finish the work ourselves and restore their treasure to them. Or again we can help them by raising the floor with a small flat stone, a pedestal from the top of which it is possible for the Beetle to continue his labours. Its use does not appear to be immediately understood, for neither of the two is in any hurry to take advantage of it. Nevertheless, by accident or design, one or other at last finds himself on the stone. Oh, joy! As he passed, he felt the ball touch his back. At that contact, courage returns; and his efforts begin once more. Standing on his helpful platform, the Scarab stretches his joints, rounds his shoulders, as one might say, and shoves the pellet upwards. When his shoulders no longer avail, he works with his legs, now upright, now head downwards. There is a fresh pause, accompanied by fresh signs of uneasiness, when the limit of extension is reached. Thereupon, without disturbing the creature, we place a second little stone on the top of the first. With the aid of this new step, which provides a fulcrum for its levers, the insect pursues its task. Thus adding story upon story as required, I have seen the Scarab, hoisted to the summit of a tottering pile three or four fingers'-breadth in height, persevere in his work until the ball was completely detached.

Had he some vague consciousness of the service performed by the gradual raising of the pedestal? I venture to doubt it, though he cleverly took advantage of my platform of little stones. As a matter of fact, if the very elementary idea of using a higher support in order to reach something placed above one's grasp were not beyond the Beetle's comprehension, how is it that, when there are two of them, neither thinks of lending the other his back so as to raise him by that much and make it possible for him to go on working? If one helped the other in this way, they could reach twice as high. They are very far, however, from any such cooperation. Each pushes the ball, with all his might, I admit, but he pushes as if he were alone and seems to have no notion of the happy result that would follow a combined effort. In this instance, when the ball is nailed to the ground by a pin, they do exactly what they do in corresponding circumstances, as, for example, when the load is brought to a standstill by some obstacle, caught in a loop of couch-grass or transfixed by some spiky bit of stalk that has run into the soft, rolling mass. I produced artificially a stoppage which is not really very different from those occurring naturally when the ball is being rolled amid the thousand and one irregularities of the ground; and the Beetle behaves, in my experimental tests, as he would have behaved in any other circumstances in which I had no part. He uses his back as a wedge and a lever and pushes with his feet, without introducing anything new into his methods, even when he has a companion and can avail himself of his assistance.

When he is all alone in face of the difficulty, when he has no assistant, his dynamic operations remain absolutely the same; and his efforts to move his transfixed ball end in success, provided that we give him the indispensable support of a platform, built up little by little. If we deny him this succour, then, no longer encouraged by the contact of his beloved ball, he loses heart and sooner or later flies away, doubtless with many regrets, and disappears. Where to? I do not know. What I do know is that he does not return with a gang of fellow-labourers whom he has begged to help him. What would he do with them, he who cannot make use of even one comrade?

But perhaps my experiment, which leaves the ball suspended at an inaccessible height and the insect with its means of action exhausted, is a little too far removed from ordinary conditions. Let us try instead a miniature pit, deep enough and steep enough to prevent the Dung-beetle, when placed at the bottom, from rolling his load up the side. These are exactly the conditions stated by Messrs. Blanchard and Illiger. Well, what happens? When dogged but utterly fruitless efforts have convinced him of his helplessness, the Beetle takes wing and disappears. Relying upon what these learned writers said, I have waited long hours for the insect to return reinforced by a few friends. I have always waited in vain. Many a time also I have found the pellet several days later just where I left it, stuck at the top of a pin or in a hole, proving that nothing fresh had happened in my absence. A ball abandoned from necessity is a ball abandoned for good, with no attempt at salvage with the aid of others. A dexterous use of wedge and lever to set the ball rolling again is therefore, when all is said, the greatest intellectual effort which I have observed in the Sacred Beetle. To make up for what the experiment refutes, namely, an appeal for help among fellow-workers, I gladly chronicle this feat of mechanical prowess for the Dung-beetles' greater glory.

Directing their steps at random, over sandy plains thick with thyme, over cart-ruts and steep places, the two Beetle brethren roll the ball along for some time, thus giving its substance a certain consistency which may be to their liking. While still on the road, they select a favourable spot. The rightful owner, the Beetle who throughout has kept the place of honour, behind the ball, the one in short who has done almost all the carting by himself, sets to work to dig the dining-room. Beside him is the ball, with number two clinging to it, shamming dead. Number one attacks the sand with his sharp-edged forehead and his toothed legs; he flings armfuls of it behind him; and the work of excavating proceeds apace. Soon the Beetle has disappeared from view in the half-dug cavern. Whenever he returns to the upper air with a load, he invariably glances at his ball to see if all is well. From time to time he brings it nearer the threshold of the burrow; he feels it and seems to acquire new vigour from the contact. The other, lying demure and motionless on the ball, continues to inspire confidence. Meanwhile the underground hall grows larger and deeper; and the digger's field of operations is now too vast for any but very occasional appearances. Now is the time. The crafty sleeper awakens and hurriedly decamps with the ball, which he pushes behind him with the speed of a pickpocket anxious not to be caught in the act. This breach of trust rouses my indignation, but the historian triumphs for the moment over the moralist and I leave him alone: I shall have time enough to intervene on the side of law and order if things threaten to turn out badly.

The thief is already some yards away. His victim comes out of the burrow, looks around and finds nothing. Doubtless an old hand himself, he knows what this means. Scent and sight soon put him on the track. He makes haste and catches up the robber; but the artful dodger, when he feels his pursuer close on his heels, promptly changes his posture, gets on his hind-legs and clasps the ball with his toothed arms, as he does when acting as an assistant.

You rogue, you! I see through your tricks: you mean to plead as an excuse that the pellet rolled down the slope and that you are only trying to stop it and bring it back home. I, however, an impartial witness, declare that the ball was quite steady at the entrance to the burrow and did not roll of its own accord. Besides, the ground is level. I declare that I saw you set the thing in motion and make off with unmistakable intentions. It was an attempt at larceny, or I've never seen one!

My evidence is not admitted. The owner cheerfully accepts the other's excuses; and the two bring the ball back to the burrow as though nothing had happened.

If the thief, however, has time to get far enough away, or if he manages to cover his trail by adroitly doubling back, the injury is irreparable. To collect provisions under a blazing sun, to cart them a long distance, to dig a comfortable banqueting-hall in the sand, and then—just when everything is ready and your appetite, whetted by exercise, lends an added charm to the approaching feast—suddenly to find yourself cheated by a crafty partner is, it must be admitted, a reverse of fortune that would dishearten most of us. The Dung-beetle does not allow himself to be cast down by this piece of ill-luck: he rubs his cheeks, spreads his antennæ, sniffs the air and flies to the nearest heap to begin all over again. I admire and envy this cast of character.

Suppose the Scarab fortunate enough to have found a loyal partner; or, better still, suppose that he has met no self-incited companion. The burrow is ready. It is a shallow cavity, about the size of one's fist, dug in soft earth, usually in sand, and communicating with the outside by a short passage just wide enough to admit the ball. As soon as the provisions are safely stored away, the Scarab shuts himself in by stopping up the entrance to his dwelling with rubbish kept in a corner for the purpose. Once the door is closed, nothing outside betrays the existence of the banqueting-chamber. And, now, hail mirth and jollity! All is for the best in the best of all possible worlds! The table is sumptuously spread; the ceiling tempers the heat of the sun and allows only a moist and gentle warmth to penetrate; the undisturbed quiet, the darkness, the Crickets' concert overhead are all pleasant aids to digestion. So complete has been the illusion that I have caught myself listening at the door, expecting to hear the revellers burst into the famous snatch in *Galatée*:8

> *Ah! qu'il est doux de ne rien faire,*
> *Quand tout s'agite autour de nous?* 9

Who would dare disturb the bliss of such a banquet? But the desire for knowledge is capable of all things; and I had the necessary daring. I will set down here the result of my violation of the home.

The ball by itself fills almost the whole room; the rich repast rises from floor to ceiling. A narrow passage runs between it and the walls. Here sit the banqueters, two at most, very often only one, belly to table, back to the wall. Once the seat is chosen, no one stirs; all the vital forces are absorbed by the digestive faculties. There is no fidgeting, which might mean the loss of a mouthful; no dainty toying with the food, which might cause some to be wasted. Everything has to pass through, properly and in order. To see them seated so solemnly around a ball of dung, one would think that they were conscious of their function as cleansers of the earth and that they were deliberately devoting themselves to that marvellous chemistry which out of filth brings forth the flower that delights our eyes and the Beetles' wing-case that jewels our lawns in spring. For this supreme work which turns into living matter the refuse which neither the Horse nor the Mule can utilize, despite the perfection of their digestive organs, the Dung-beetle must needs be specially equipped. And indeed anatomy compels us to admire the prodigious length of his coiled intestine, which slowly elaborates the materials in its manifold windings and exhausts them to the very last serviceable atom. Matter from which the ruminant's stomach could extract nothing, yields to this powerful alembic riches that, at a mere touch, are transmuted into ebon mail in the Sacred Scarab and a breastplate of gold and rubies in other Dung-beetles.

Now this wonderful metamorphosis of ordure has to be accomplished in the shortest possible time: the public health demands it. And so the Scarab is endowed with matchless digestive powers. Once housed in the company of food, he goes on eating and digesting, day and night, until the provisions are exhausted. There is no difficulty in proving this. Open the cell to which the Dung-beetle has retired from the world. At any hour of the day, we shall find the insect seated at table and, behind it, still hanging to it, a continuous cord, roughly coiled like a pile of cables. One can easily guess, without embarrassing explanations, what this cord represents. The great ball of dung passes mouthful by mouthful through the Beetle's digestive canals, yielding up its nutritive essences, and reappears at the opposite end spun into a cord. Well, this unbroken cord, which is always found hanging from the aperture of the draw-plate, is ample proof, without further evidence, that the digestive processes go on without ceasing. When the provisions are coming to an end, the cable unrolled is of an astounding length: it can be measured in feet. Where shall we find the like of this stomach which, to avoid any loss when life's balance-sheet is made out, feasts for a week or a fortnight, without stopping, on such distasteful fare?

When the whole ball has passed through the machine, the hermit comes back to the daylight, tries his luck afresh, finds another patch of dung, fashions a new ball and starts eating again. This life of pleasure lasts for a month or two, from May to June; then, with the coming of the fierce heat beloved of the Cicadæ,10 the Sacred Beetles take up their summer quarters and bury themselves in the cool earth. They reappear with the first autumn rains, less numerous and less active than in spring, but now seemingly absorbed in the most important work of all, the future of the species.

1 A village in the department of the Gard, facing Avignon.—*Author's Note.*

2 'When you and I start housekeeping, alas, what shall we do?
You in front and I behind, we'll shove the tub along!'

3 Pierre Joseph Proudhon (1809–1865), the French socialist, author of *Qu'est-ce que la propriété?* etc.—*Translator's Note.*

4 Émile Blanchard (b. 1819), a French naturalist, best known by his works on entomology.—*Translator's Note.*

5 The Scarabæi also bear the name of Ateuchus.—*Author's Note.*

6 Johann Karl Wilhelm Illiger (1775–1813), a German naturalist, editor of a *Magasin für Insektenkunde* and author of *Prodromus systematis mammalium et avium,* etc.—*Translator's Note.*

7 *Gymnopleurus pilularius* is a Dung-beetle nearly related to the Sacred Beetle, but smaller. As his name suggests, he also rolls pellets of dung. The Gymnopleurus is very general, even in the north, whereas *Scarabæus sacer* is hardly ever found away from the shores of the Mediterranean.—*Author's Note.*

8 A light opera, with music by Victor Massé and libretto by Jules Barbier and Michel Carré (1852).—*Translator's Note.*

9 'Ah, how sweet is *far niente,*
When round us throbs the busy world!'

10 Cf. *The Life of the Grasshopper,* by J. Henri Fabre, translated by Alexander Teixeira de Mattos: chaps. i. to v.—*Translator's Note.*

CHAPTER II
THE SACRED BEETLE IN CAPTIVITY

If we ransack the books for information about the habits of the dung-rollers in general and the Sacred Beetle in particular, we find that modern science still clings to some of the beliefs which were current in the days of the Pharaohs. We are told that the ball which is bumped across the fields contains an egg, that it is a cradle in which the future larva is to find both board and lodging. The parents roll it over hilly country to make it nice and round; and, when jolts and jars and tumbles down steep places have shaped it properly, they bury it and abandon it to the care of that great incubator, the earth.

So rough an upbringing has always seemed to me improbable. How could a Beetle's egg, that delicate thing, so sensitive under its soft wrapper, survive the shaking-up which it would undergo in that rolling cradle? In the germ is a spark of life which the least touch, the veriest trifle can extinguish. Are we to believe that the parents would deliberately bump it over hill and dale for hours? No, that is not the way in which things happen; a mother does not subject her offspring to the torture of a Regulus' barrel.

However, something more than logic was needed to make a clean sweep of accepted opinion. I therefore opened some hundreds of the pellets that were being rolled along by the Dung-beetles; I opened others which I took from holes dug before my eyes; and never once did I find either a central cell or an egg in those pellets. They were invariably rough lumps of food, fashioned in haste, with no definite internal structure, merely so much provender with which the Beetle retires to spend a few days in undisturbed gluttony. The dung-rollers covet and steal them from one another with a keenness which they would certainly not display in robbing one another of new family charges. For Sacred Beetles to go stealing eggs would be an absurdity, each of them having quite enough to do in securing the future of her own. So this point is henceforward settled beyond question: the pellets which we see the Dung-beetles rolling never contain eggs.

My first attempt to solve the knotty problem of the larva's rearing involved the construction of a spacious vivarium, with an artificial soil of sand and a constant supply of provisions. Into this cage I put some twenty Sacred Beetles, together with Copres, Gymnopleuri and Onthophagi. No entomological experiment ever cost me so many disappointments. The difficulty was the renewing of the food supply. Now my landlord owned a stable and a Horse. I gained the confidence of his man, who at first laughed at my proposals, but soon allowed himself to be convinced by the sight of silver. Each of my insects' breakfasts came to twenty-five centimes. I am sure that no Beetle budget ever amounted to such a sum before. Well, I can still see and I shall always see Joseph, after grooming the Horse of a morning, put his head over the garden-wall and, making a speaking-trumpet of his hand, call 'Hi!' to me in a whisper. I would hurry up to receive a potful of droppings. Caution was necessary on both sides, as the sequel will show you. One day the master happened to come up just when the transfer was being made, and took it into his head that all his manure was going over the wall and that what he wanted for his cabbages went to grow my verbenas and narcissi. Vainly I tried to explain: he thought that I was being funny. Poor Joseph was scolded, called all manner of names and threatened with dismissal if it happened again. It didn't.

I had one resource left, which was to go ignominiously along the high-road and furtively collect my captives' daily bread in a paper bag. This I did and I am not ashamed of it. Sometimes fortune favoured me: a Donkey carrying the produce of the Château-Renard or Barbentane kitchen-gardens to the Avignon market would drop his contribution as he passed my door. The gratuity, picked up instantly, made me rich for several days. In short, by scheming, waiting, running about and playing the diplomat for a blob of dung, I managed to feed my prisoners. If a passion for one's work and a love which nothing can discourage ensure success, my experiment ought to have succeeded. It did not succeed. After a time, my Sacred Beetles, pining for their native heath in a space too limited for their elaborate evolutions, died miserable deaths, without revealing their secrets. The Gymnopleuri and Onthophagi were not so disappointing. At the proper time I shall make use of the information which I obtained from them.

Together with my attempts at home breeding I carried on my direct investigations abroad. The results fell far short of my wishes. One day I decided that I must enlist outside help. As it happened, a merry band of youngsters was crossing the plateau. It was a Thursday.1 Untroubled by thoughts of school and horrid lessons, they were coming from the neighbouring village of Les Angles, with an apple in one hand and a piece of bread in the other, and wending their way to the bare hill yonder, where the bullets bury themselves harmlessly when the garrison is at rifle-practice. The object of this early morning expedition was the unearthing of a few bits of lead, worth perhaps a halfpenny the lot. The small pink blossoms of the wild geranium decked the scanty patches of grass which for a brief moment beautified this Arabia Petræa; the Wheat-ear, in his black-and-white motley, twittered as he flew from one rocky point to another; on the threshold of burrows dug at the foot of the thyme-tufts, the Crickets were filling the air with their droning symphony. And the children were rejoicing in this springtide happiness and rejoicing still more in the prospect of wealth, the halfpenny which they would receive for such bullets as they found, the halfpenny which would enable them to buy two peppermint bull's-eyes next Sunday, two of the big ones, at a farthing apiece, from the woman at the stall outside the church.

I accost the tallest, whose sharp face gives me some hope of him; the little ones stand round, eating their apples. I explain what I want and show them the Sacred Beetle rolling his ball; I tell them that in some such ball, hidden somewhere or other underground, there is occasionally a little hollow place and in that hollow a little worm. The thing to do is to dig around at random, keeping an eye on what the Beetles are doing, and to find the ball containing the worm. Balls without a worm don't count. And, to tempt them with a fabulous sum which shall divert to my purposes the time hitherto devoted to a few farthings' worth of lead, I promise to pay a franc, a shiny new twenty-sou piece, for each occupied ball. At the mention of this sum, those adorably innocent eyes open their widest. I have upset all their ideas of finance by naming this fanciful price. Then, to show that my proposal is serious, I distribute a few sous as earnest-money. I arrange to be there next week, on the same day and at the same time, and faithfully to perform my part of the bargain towards all those who have made the lucky find. After carefully posting the party in their duties, I dismiss them.

'He means it!' the children said, as they went away. 'He really means it! If only we could make a franc apiece!'

And their hearts swelling with fond hopes, they clinked the sous in their hands. The flattened bullets were forgotten. I saw the children scatter over the plain and begin their search.

On the appointed day, a week later, I returned to the plateau. I was confident of success. My young helpers were sure to have spoken to their playmates of this lucrative trade in Beetle-balls and convinced the incredulous by displaying their earnest-money. And indeed I found a larger party than the first time awaiting me on the spot. They came running to meet me, but there was no burst of triumph, no shout of joy. I suspected at once that things were going badly; and my suspicions were but too well-founded. Many times, after coming out of school, they had hunted for what I had described, but they had never discovered anything like it. They handed me a few pellets found underground with the Beetle, but these were simply masses of provisions, containing no larva. I explained matters anew and made another appointment for the following Thursday. Again the search was unsuccessful. The disheartened little hunters were now reduced to quite a small number. I made a final appeal to their sportsmanship and perseverance; but nothing came of it. And I ended by compensating the most industrious, those who had held out to the last, and cancelling the bargain. I had to conduct my own researches, which, though apparently very simple, were in reality extremely difficult.

Many years have passed since then, but even to-day I am without any definite, consistent result after all my digging and exploring, though I have made my examinations at the most likely spots and have carefully watched for favourable opportunities. I am reduced to piecing together my incomplete observations and filling up the gaps by analogy.2 The little that I have seen, combined with my study of other Dung-beetles in captivity—Gymnopleuri, Copres and Onthophagi—is summed up in what follows.

The ball which is destined to contain the egg is not made in public, in the hurry and confusion of the dung-yard. It is a work of art and supreme patience, demanding concentration and scrupulous care, both alike impossible in the thick of the crowd. One needs solitude in order to think out a plan of operations and set to work. So the mother digs in the sand a burrow four to eight inches deep. It is a rather spacious hall communicating with the outer world by a much narrower passage. The insect brings into it carefully selected materials, doubtless in spherical form. There must be many journeys, for towards the end of the work the contents of the cell are out of all proportion to the size of the entrance-door and could not be stored at one attempt. I remember a Spanish Copris who, at the time of my inspection, was finishing a ball as big as an orange at the far end of a burrow whose only communication with the outside was by means of a gallery into which I was just able to insert my finger. It is true that the Copres do not roll pills and do not travel long distances to fetch food home. They dig a hole immediately under the dung and drag the material backwards, armful by armful, to the bottom of their well. They have thus no difficulty in provisioning their houses; moreover, they work in security under the shelter of the manure: two conditions that promote luxurious tastes. The Dung-beetles that follow the humble trade of pill-rollers are less extravagant; and yet, if he cares to make two or three journeys, the Sacred Beetle can amass wealth of which the Spanish Copris might well be jealous.

So far, the Beetle has only raw material, lumped together anyhow. A minute sorting has to take place before anything else is done: this stuff, the purest, is for the inner layer on which the grub will feed; that other, coarser stuff is for the outer layers, which are not meant for food and serve only as a protecting shell. Then, around a central hollow which receives the egg, the materials must be arranged in successive strata, according as they are less refined and less nutritive; the layers must possess a proper consistency and must be made to adhere to one another; last of all, the stringy parts of the outer layers, which have to protect the whole structure, must be felted together. How does the clumsy Sacred Beetle, who is so stiff in her movements, accomplish a work of this kind in complete darkness, at the bottom of a hole crammed with provisions and hardly leaving room to stir? When I consider the delicacy of the workmanship and then the rough tools of the worker—angular limbs capable of cutting into hard or even rocky soil—I think of an Elephant trying to make lace. Let whoso can explain this miracle of maternal industry; as for me, I give it up, all the more as I have not had the luck to see the artist at work. We will confine ourselves to describing her masterpiece.

The ball containing the egg is usually the size of an average apple. In the centre is an oval hollow about two-fifths of an inch in diameter. The egg is fixed at the bottom, standing perpendicularly; it is cylindrical, rounded at both ends, yellowish-white and about as large as a grain of wheat, but shorter. The inside of the niche is coated with a shiny, greenish-brown, semifluid material, a real stercoral cream, destined to form the larva's first mouthfuls. To make this dainty food, does the mother collect the quintessence of the dung? The appearance of it tells me something different and makes me certain that it is a pap prepared in the maternal stomach. The Pigeon softens the grain in her crop and turns it into a sort of milky soup which she subsequently disgorges to her brood. To all seeming, the Dung-beetle displays the same solicitude: she half-digests choice provender and disgorges it in the form of a meat-extract with which she lines the walls of the cavity where the egg is laid. Thus the larva, on hatching, finds an easily-digested food, which very soon strengthens its stomach and enables it to attack the underlying strata, which have not been refined in the same way. Under the semi-fluid paste is a soft, well-compressed, uniform mass, from which every stringy particle is excluded. Beyond this are the coarser layers, abounding in vegetable fibres. Finally, the outside of the ball is composed of the commonest materials, but packed and felted into a stout rind.

Manifestly we have here a progressive change of diet. On leaving the egg, the frail grub licks the dainty broth on the walls of its cell. There is not much of this, but it is strengthening and very nutritious. The pap of earliest infancy is followed by the more solid food given to the weaned nurseling, a sort of paste that stands midway between the exquisitely delicate fare at the start and the coarse provisions at the finish. There is a thick layer of it, enough to turn the infant into a sturdy youngster. But now for the strong comes strong meat: barley-bread with its husks, that is to say, natural droppings full of sharp bits of hay. Of this the larva has enough and to spare; and, when it has attained its full growth, there remains an enclosing layer. The capacity of the dwelling has increased with the growth of the occupant, fed on the very substance of the walls; the original little cell with the very thick walls is now a big cell with walls only a few millimetres in thickness; the inner layers have become larva, nymph or Beetle, according to the period. Lastly, the ball itself is a stout shell, protecting within its spacious interior the mysterious processes of the metamorphosis.

I can go no farther, for lack of observations; my records of the birth of the Sacred Beetle stop short at the egg. I have not seen the larva, which however is known and is described in the text-books;3 nor have I seen the perfect insect while still enclosed in its chamber in the ball, before it has had any practice in its duties as a pill-roller and excavator. And this is just what I particularly wanted to see. I should have liked to find the Dung-beetle in his native cell, recently transformed, new to all labour, so as to examine the workman's hand before it started its work. I will tell you the reason for this wish.

Insects have at the end of each leg a sort of finger, or tarsus as it is called, consisting of a succession of delicate parts which may be compared with the joints of our fingers. They end in a hooked claw. One finger to each leg: that is the rule; and this finger, at least with the higher Beetles and notably the Dung-beetles, has five phalanges or joints. Now, by a really strange exception, the Scarabs have no tarsi on their front legs, while possessing very well-shaped ones, with five joints apiece, on the two other pairs. They are maimed, crippled: they lack, on their fore-limbs, that which in the insect very roughly represents our hand. A similar anomaly occurs in the Onitis- and Bubas-beetles, who also belong to the Dung-beetle family. Entomology has long recorded this curious fact, without being able to offer a satisfactory explanation. Is the creature born maimed, does it come into the world without fingers to its forelimbs? Or does it lose them by accident, once it is given over to its toilsome labours?

One could easily imagine this mutilation to be the result of the insect's hard work. Poking about, digging and raking and slicing, at one time in the gravelly soil, at another in the stringy mass of manure, do not constitute a task in which organs so delicate as the tarsi can be employed without risk. And here is an even more serious matter: when the Beetle is rolling his ball backwards, with his head down, it is with the extremities of his fore-feet that he presses against the ground. What might not happen to the insect's feeble fingers, slender as thread, in consequence of this continual rubbing against the rough soil? They are merely useless encumbrances; one day or other they seem bound to disappear, crushed, torn off, worn out in a thousand ways. We know unfortunately that our own workmen are all too frequently injured in handling heavy tools and lifting great weights; even so might the Scarab be crippled in rolling his ball, an enormous load to him. In that case his maimed arms would be a noble testimony to his industrious life.

But straightway grave doubts begin to assail us. If these mutilations were really accidental and the result of too strenuous work, they would be the exception, not the rule. Because a workman or several workmen have had a hand caught and crushed in a machine, it does not follow that all the rest will also lose their hands. If the Scarab sometimes, or even very frequently, loses his fore-fingers in pursuing his trade as a pill-roller, there must be some at least who, more fortunate or more skilful, have preserved their tarsi. Let us then consult the actual facts. I have observed in very large numbers the various species of Scarabs that inhabit France: *Scarabæus sacer*, who is common in Provence; *S. semipunctatus*, who keeps fairly close to the sea and frequents the sandy shores of Cette, Palavas and the Golfe Juan; lastly, *S. laticollis*, who is much more widely distributed than either of the others and is found up the Rhone Valley at least as far as Lyons. In addition, I have studied an African species, *S. cicatricosus*, picked up near Constantine. Well, in all four species, the absence of tarsi on the front legs has been an invariable fact, with not a single exception, at any rate within the range of my observations. The Scarab therefore is maimed from the start; and it is a natural peculiarity in his case, not an accident.

Besides, there is another argument in support of this statement. If the lack of fore-fingers were an accidental mutilation, due to violent exertion, there are other insects, Dung-beetles too, who habitually undertake works of excavation even more arduous than the Scarab's, and who ought therefore, *a fortiori*, to be deprived of their front tarsi, since these are useless and even irksome when the leg has to serve as a powerful digging-implement. The Geotrupes, for instance, who so well deserve their name, meaning Earth-piercers, sink wells in the hard soil of the roads, among stones cemented with clay: perpendicular wells so deep that, to inspect the cell at the bottom of them, we have to make use of a stout spade; and even then we do not always succeed. Now these unrivalled miners, who easily open up long tunnels in a substance whose surface the Sacred Beetle would hardly be able to disturb, have their front tarsi intact, as if cutting through rocks were work calling for delicate tools rather than strong ones. Everything then supports the belief that, if we could see the Scarab while still a novice in his native cell, we should find him to be mutilated in just the same way as the much-travelled veteran who has worn himself out with toil.

This absence of fingers might serve as the foundation for an argument in favour of the theories now in fashion: the struggle for life and the evolution of the species. People might say:

'The Scarabs began by having tarsi to all their legs, in conformity with the general laws of insect structure. In one way or another, some of them lost these troublesome appendages to their front legs, they being hurtful rather than useful. Finding themselves the better for this mutilation, which made their work easier, they gained the advantage over their less-favoured fellows; they founded a family by handing down their fingerless stumps to their descendants; and the fingered insect of antiquity ended by becoming the maimed insect of our times.'

I am ready to yield to this reasoning if you will first tell me why, with similar but much harder tasks to perform, the Geotrupes has retained his tarsi. Until then we will go on believing that the first Scarab who rolled his ball, perhaps on the shore of some lake in which the Palæotherium bathed, was as innocent of front tarsi as his descendant of to-day.

1 The weekly holiday in the French schools.—*Translator's Note.*

2 This seems the place in which to remind the reader that the first two chapters of the present volume correspond with Chapters I. and II. of the first volume of the *Souvenirs entomologiques* in their original form. Chapters III. to VII. of the present volume are translations of Chapters I. to V. of the fifth volume of the *Souvenirs,* published many years later, at a time when Fabre had completed his study of the Sacred Beetle.—*Translator's Note.*

3 Cf. Mulsant's *Coléoptères de France: Lamellicornes.—Author's Note.*

CHAPTER III
THE SACRED BEETLE: THE BALL

There is no need to return to the Sacred Beetle working in the daylight or consuming his booty underground, either alone, as usually happens, or in the company of a guest: what I have said about this in a former chapter is enough; and further observations would give no new information of special interest. There is only one point which deserves attention. This is the method of constructing the spherical pellet, consisting merely of provisions which the Beetle collects for his own use and conveys to an underground dining-room excavated at a convenient spot. My present cages, which are much better arranged than those which I had at first, enable us to watch the operation at our leisure; and this operation will furnish data which will be of the greatest value later in explaining the mysterious structure of the nest. Let us then once more watch the Sacred Beetle as he busies himself with his victuals.

I supply fresh provisions, derived from the Mule or, better, the Sheep. The scent of the heap carries the news far and wide. The Beetles hasten up from every direction, extending and waving the russet feathers of their antennæ, a sign of acute excitement. Those who were dozing underground split the sandy ceiling and sally forth from their cellars. They are now all at the banquet, not without quarrels among neighbours, who fight for the best bits and knock one another over with sudden back-handers from their broad fore-legs. Things calm down; and, without further disputes for the moment, each gets all that he can out of the spot where he happens to be.

The foundation of the structure is, as a rule, a bit that is almost round of itself. This is the kernel which, enlarged by successive layers, will become the ultimate ball, the size of an apricot. Having tested it and found it suitable, the owner leaves it as it is; or, at other times, he may clean it a little, scraping the outside, which is rough with bits of sand. It is now a question of constructing the ball upon this foundation. The tools are the six-toothed rake of the semicircular shield and the broad shovels of the fore-legs, which are likewise armed on the outer edge with strong teeth, five in number.

Without for a moment letting go of the kernel, which is held in his four hind-legs, more particularly those of the third, the longest pair, the Beetle turns round slowly from side to side on the top of his embryo pellet and selects from the heap around him the materials for increasing its size. His sharp-edged forehead peels, cuts, digs and rakes; his fore-legs work in unison, gathering and drawing up an armful which is at once placed upon the central mass and patted down. A few vigorous applications of the toothed shovels press the new layer into position. And so, with armful after armful carefully added on top, beneath and at the sides, the original pill grows into a big ball.

While working, the builder never leaves the dome of his edifice: he revolves on his own axis, if he wants to give his attention to any lateral part; to shape the lower portion, he bends down to the point where it touches the ground; but from beginning to end the sphere never moves on its base and the Beetle never relaxes his hold.

To obtain a perfectly round form, we need the potter's wheel, whose rotation makes up for our want of skill; to enlarge his snowball and make it into the enormous sphere which he will end by being unable to move, the schoolboy rolls it in the snow: the rolling gives it the regularity which the direct work of the hands, guided by an inexperienced eye, would not. More dexterous than we, the Sacred Beetle can dispense with either rolling or rotation; he moulds his ball by means of superadded layers, without shifting its place and without even descending for an instant from the top of his dome to view the whole structure from the requisite distance. The compasses of his bow-legs, a living pair of callipers which measure and check the curve, are sufficient for his purpose.

It is only with extreme caution, however, that I introduce these callipers, as I am perfectly convinced, by a host of facts, that instinct has no need of special tools. If further proof were wanted, here it is. The male Scarab's hind-legs are perceptibly bowed; the female's, on the contrary, are almost straight, though she is much the cleverer and is able, as we shall see presently, to produce masterpieces whose exquisite form far surpasses that of a monotonous sphere.

If the curved compasses play but a secondary part in the matter and perhaps no part at all, what is the guiding principle of this sphericity? If one merely took into consideration the insect's organism and the circumstances in which the work is done, I see absolutely none. We must go back farther, we must go back to the innate genius, the instinct that guides the tool. The Scarab has a natural gift for making spheres, just as the Hive-bee has a natural gift for making hexagonal prisms. Both achieve geometrical perfection in their work and are independent of any special mechanism which would force upon them the particular shape attained.

For the time being, keep this in mind: the Sacred Beetle makes his ball by placing next to each other armful after armful of the materials which he has collected; he builds it up without moving it, without turning it round.

He fashions the dung with the pressure of his fore-arms as the modeller in our studios fashions his clay with the pressure of his thumb. And the result is not an approximate sphere, with a lumpy surface; it is a perfect sphere, which our human manufacturers would not disown.

The time has come for retiring with the booty so that we may bury it farther away, at no great depth, and consume it in peace. The owner, therefore, draws his ball out of the dung-yard; and, in accordance with ancient usage, begins straightway to roll it about on the ground, a little at random. Any one who was not present at the beginning and who now saw the ball rolling along, with the insect pushing it backwards, would naturally imagine that the round shape resulted from this method of transport. It rolls, therefore it becomes round, even as a shapeless lump of clay would soon become round if trundled in the same way. Though apparently logical, the idea is erroneous in every respect: we have just seen this perfect sphericity acquired before the ball moved from the spot. The rolling therefore has nothing to do with this geometrical accuracy; it merely hardens the surface into a tough crust and polishes it a little, if only by working into the substance of the pellet any coarse bits that might have made it rough at the beginning. Between the pill that has been rolled for hours and the pill that is stationary in the dung-yard there is no difference in configuration.

What is the advantage of this particular shape, which is invariably adopted at the very outset of the work? Does the Scarab derive any benefit from the circular form? Your spectacles would have to be made of walnut-shells if you failed to see that the insect is brilliantly inspired when it kneads its cake into a ball. These victuals, the meagrest of meagre pittances from the point of view of nourishment, for the Sheep's fourfold stomach has already extracted pretty nearly all the assimilable matter, have to make up in quantity for what they lack in quality.

It is the same with various other Dung-beetles. They are all insatiable gluttons; they all need a much larger amount of food than their modest dimensions would lead us to suspect. The Spanish Copris, no bigger than a good-sized hazel-nut, accumulates underground, for a single meal, a pie as big as my fist; the Stercoraceous Geotrupes hoards in his hole a sausage nine inches long and as wide as the neck of a claret-bottle.

These mighty eaters have an easy time of it. They establish themselves immediately under the heap dropped by some standing Mule. Here they dig passages and dining-rooms. The provisions are at the door of the house; they form a roof for it. All that you have to do is to bring them in, armful by armful, taking only as much as you can carry comfortably, for you can go on fetching more as long as you like. In this way, scandalous quantities of food are unobtrusively stored away in peaceful manors whose presence no outward sign betrays.

The Sacred Beetle is not so fortunate as to have his cottage underneath the heap where the victuals are collected. He is of a vagabond temperament; and, when his work is over, he has no great inclination for the company of those arrant thieves, his kinsmen. He has therefore to travel to a distance with what he has secured, in quest of a site where he can establish himself alone. His stock of provisions, it is true, is comparatively modest: it is not to be mentioned in the same breath as the Copris' enormous cakes or the Geotrupes' fat sausages. No matter: modest though it be, its weight and bulk are too much for the strength of any Beetle that might think of carrying it direct. It is too heavy, ever so much too heavy, for him to take between his legs and fly away with, nor could he possibly drag it, gripped in his mandibles.

If the hermit, eager to withdraw from the world, wished to make use of direct means of conveyance, there would be only one method by which he could accumulate in his far-off cell food enough for even a single day: that would be to carry load after load on the wing, each load being proportionate to his strength. But what a number of journeys that would involve! What a lot of time would be wasted in this piecemeal harvesting! Besides, when he went back, would he not find the table already cleared? Think of the number of guests who were giving it their attention! The opportunity is a good one; it may not occur again for a long while. We must make the most of it without delay; the thing to do is to secure enough now to stock our larder for at least a day.

But how to set about it? Nothing could be simpler. What we cannot carry we drag; what we cannot drag we cart by rolling it along, as witness all our wheeled conveyances. The Sacred Beetle therefore chooses the sphere as a means of transport. It is the best shape of all for rolling; it needs no axle-tree; it adapts itself admirably to the diverse inequalities of the ground and, at each point of its surface, provides the necessary leverage for the least expenditure of effort. Such is the mechanical problem which the pill-roller solves. The spherical form of his treasure is not the effect of the rolling: it precedes it; it is modelled precisely with a view to that method of conveyance, which is to make the carriage of the heavy load feasible.

The Sacred Beetle is a passionate lover of the sun, whose image he copies in the radiating notches of his rounded shield. He needs the bright light in order to make the most of the heap whence he extracts first provisions and next materials for nest-building. The other Dung-beetles—Geotrupes, Copres, Onites, Onthophagi—for the most part have dark, mysterious habits; they work unseen under the roof of excrement; they do not begin their quest until night is at hand and the last glimmer of twilight is fading. The more trustful Scarab both seeks and finds amid the gladness of the noonday sun; he works his bit of ground quite openly and reaps his harvest in the hottest and brightest hours of the day. His ebon breastplate is glittering on top of the heap at times when there is naught to indicate the presence of numerous fellow-workers, belonging to other genera, who are busy underneath, carving themselves their share of the lower strata. Darkness for others, but for him the light!

This love of the unscreened sun has its blissful side, as the insect, drunk with heat, shows from time to time by exultant transports; but it has also certain disadvantages. I have never witnessed any quarrel at harvest-time between next-door neighbours, when these were Copres or Geotrupes. Working in the dark, each is ignorant of what is happening beside him. The rich morsel secured by one of them cannot arouse the envy of his neighbours, since it is not perceived. This perhaps explains the pacific relations among Dung-beetles who work in the gloomy depths of the heap.

My suspicions are not unfounded. Robbery, the execrable right of the strongest, is not the exclusive prerogative of the human brute: animals also practise it; and the Sacred Beetle is a notorious offender. As the work is done in the open, every one knows or is able to find out what his companions are doing. They are mutually envious of each other's pills; and scuffles take place between proprietors wishing to leave the yard and plunderers who find it more convenient to rob their fellows than to set to work and knead loaves for themselves. On guard on the top of his treasure, the owner of a ball will face his assailant, who is trying to climb up, and push him into space with a stroke from his stout fore-arms. The thief is flung on his back and flounders about for a moment, but he is soon up and back again. The struggle is renewed. Right does not always win, in which case the robber makes off with his prize and the victim returns to the heap to make himself another pill. It is not unusual for a third thief to appear upon the scene during the fight and settle matters between the litigants by carrying off the property at issue. I am inclined to think that it was affrays of this sort that gave rise to the childish story of the Sacred Beetles who were called to the rescue and came to lend a hand to their brothers in distress. Brazen footpads were taken for kindly helpers.

The Sacred Beetle then is an inveterate thief; he shares the tastes of the Bedouin Arab, his fellow-countryman in Africa; he too is addicted to raiding. In his case, hunger and dearth, both evil counsellors, cannot be invoked as an explanation of this moral obliquity. Provisions are plentiful in my cages; certainly, in their days of liberty, my captives never lived in the midst of such abundance; and yet affrays are of frequent occurrence. They fight hotly-contested battles for the loaves, just as though bread were lacking. Poverty has nothing to do with it, for very often the thief abandons his booty after rolling it for a few seconds. They steal for the pleasure of stealing. As La Fontaine1 well says, there is

... double profit à faire:

*Son bien premièrement; et puis le mal d'autrui.*2

In view of this propensity for thieving, what is the best thing that a Scarab can do when he has conscientiously made his ball? Obviously, to shun his fellows, to leave the premises and get away to a distant spot where he can consume his provisions in the depths of some hiding-place. This is what he does; and he loses no time in doing it: he knows his kinsmen too well.

Here we see the necessity for an easy method of conveyance, so that sufficient provisions may be carted in a single journey and as swiftly as possible. The Sacred Beetle likes working in the bright light, in the sunshine. His profits therefore, made in full view of everybody, are no secret to any of the workers who have hurried to the same heap. Thus is envy kindled; thus it becomes imperative to retire to a distance, in order to avoid being robbed. This speedy retreat demands a convenient means of transport; and that is obtained by the spherical form given to the materials collected.

Here is the conclusion, unexpected but very logical and I would even say obvious: the Sacred Beetle shapes his provisions into a ball because he is an ardent lover of the sun. The various Dung-beetles who work in broad daylight, the Gymnopleuri and Sisyphi of my district, conform to the same mechanical principle: they all know the advantages of a sphere, the best rolling-apparatus; they all practise the art of pill-making. The other Dung-beetles, who work in the dark, do nothing of the kind: their accumulations of food are shapeless.

Life in the vivarium supplies us with some other facts which are not undeserving of the commentator's attention. We have said that, when fresh provisions are supplied, the Sacred Beetles who are roaming about come running up eagerly to the smoking fare. The rich effluvia also speedily attract those who are slumbering in their burrows. Little mounds of sand pop up here and there, cracking as though for an eruption, and we see new guests emerge, wiping the dust from their eyes with the flat of their feet. Neither their dozing in that underground room nor the thick roof of their dwelling has succeeded in foiling their keenness of scent: those who have had to unearth themselves reach the lump almost as quickly as the others.

These details remind us of certain facts noted, not without surprise, by a host of observers on the sunny beaches at Cette, Palavas, the Golfe Juan and the North African coast, down to the lonely Sahara. Here the Sacred Beetle and his kinsmen—the Half-spotted Scarab, the Pock-marked Scarab and others—swarm, becoming more vigorous and more active in proportion as the climate grows hotter. They abound; and yet very often not one shows himself; the entomologist's practised eye fails to discover a single specimen.

But now see things change. Seized with an urgent physiological need, you leave your party unobtrusively and retire behind the bushes. You have hardly stood up, hardly begun to adjust your dress, when—whoosh!—here comes one, here come three, here come ten, appearing suddenly you know not whence, and swoop upon the provender. Have they hastened from afar, these bustling scavengers? Certainly not. Had they been apprised at a great distance by their sense of smell, which is not in itself impossible, they would not have had time to reach the quite recent windfall so promptly. It follows, therefore, that they were close by, within a radius of ten or twenty yards, hidden underground and dozing. A scent that is ever awake, even in the lethargy of sleep, told them, down in their burrows, of the happy event; and, splitting their ceilings, they hurry up forthwith. In less time than the incident takes to relate, a swarming population enlivens what was but now a desert.

A keen and vigilant scent is the Beetle's, we must admit; a scent which is always in operation. The Dog smells the truffle through the soil, but he is awake; the pill-roller smells his favourite fare through the ground in the opposite direction, but he is asleep. Which of the two has the subtler scent?

Science flings wide her net, welcoming even filth; and truth soars at heights where nothing can soil her. The reader will therefore be good enough to excuse certain details which cannot be avoided in a history of the Dung-beetle; he will show some indulgence for what has gone before and what will follow. The revolting workshop of the insect that manipulates ordure will lead perhaps to loftier ideas than would the perfumer's factory with its jasmine and patchouli.

I have accused the Sacred Beetle of being an insatiable gormandizer. It is time to prove what I said. In my cages, which are too small to allow of much pill-rolling, my boarders often scorn to accumulate provisions and confine themselves to eating where they are. It is a good opportunity for us: the meal taken in public will tell us better than the underground banquet what a Dung-beetle's stomach can do.

On a very still and sultry day—these are the conditions most favourable to my anchorites' gastronomic joys—I observe one of the diners in the open air, from eight o'clock in the morning until eight o'clock at night. Watch in hand, I time the glutton. He appears to have come across a morsel greatly to his taste, for, during those twelve hours, he never stops feasting, but remains glued to the table, absolutely stationary. At eight o'clock in the evening, I pay him a last visit. His appetite seems undiminished; I find him in as fine fettle as at the start. The banquet then must have gone on some time longer, until the dish had disappeared entirely. In fact, next morning there was no sign of my Beetle; and, of the sumptuous repast begun on the previous day, naught remained but crumbs.

To eat the clock round is no small feat of gluttony; but the present instance shows a much more remarkable feat of digestion. While matter is continuously being chewed and swallowed by the insect in front, it is reappearing, no less continuously, behind, deprived of its nutritive particles and spun into a thin black cord, similar to cobbler's thread. The Scarab never evacuates except at table, so quickly are his digestive operations performed. The wire-drawing apparatus begins to work at the first few mouthfuls; it ceases soon after the last. Without a break from beginning to end of the meal, the slender cord, ever appended to the discharging orifice, goes on piling itself into a heap which can easily be unrolled so long as there is no sign of desiccation.

The working is as regular as that of a chronometer. Every minute, or rather, to be exact, every four-and-fifty seconds, a discharge takes place and the thread is lengthened by three to four millimetres.3 At long intervals I employ my tweezers, remove the cord and unroll the mass along a graduated rule, in order to measure the amount produced. The total for twelve hours is 2·88 metres.4 As the meal and its necessary complement, the work of the digestive apparatus, went on for some time longer after my last visit, which was paid at eight o'clock in the evening by lantern-light, my Beetle must have spun an unbroken stercoraceous cord well over three yards in length.

Given the diameter and the length of the thread, it is easy to calculate its volume. Nor is it difficult to arrive at the exact volume of the insect by measuring the quantity of water which it displaces when immersed in a narrow cylinder. The figures thus obtained are not devoid of interest: they tell us that, at a single bout of eating, in a dozen hours, the Sacred Beetle digests very nearly his own bulk in food. What a stomach! And, above all, what rapidity, what power of digestion! From the very first mouthfuls, the residuum forms itself into a thread that stretches and stretches indefinitely as long as the meal lasts. In that amazing laboratory, which perhaps never puts up its shutters, unless it be when victuals are lacking, the material merely passes through, is at once treated by the stomach's reagents and at once exhausted. One may well believe that an apparatus which sanifies filth so quickly has some part to play in the public health. We shall have occasion to return to this important subject.

1 Jean de La Fontaine (1621–1695), author of the famous *Fables.—Translator's Note.*

2 '… a double chance of gain:

First, one's own profit; next, another's loss.'

3 ·11 to ·15 inch.—*Translator's Note.*

4 Close upon 9½ feet.—*Translator's Note.*

CHAPTER IV
THE SACRED BEETLE: THE PEAR

The young shepherd who had been told in his spare time to watch the doings of the Sacred Beetle came to me in high spirits, one Sunday in the latter part of June, to say that he thought the time had come to begin our investigations. He had detected the insect issuing from the ground, had dug at the spot where it made its appearance, and had found, at no great depth, the queer thing which he was bringing me.

Queer it was and calculated to upset the little that I thought I knew. In shape, it was exactly like a tiny pear that had lost all its fresh colour and turned brown in rotting. What could this curious object be, this pretty plaything that seemed to have come from a turner's workshop? Was it made by human hands? Was it a model of the fruit of the pear-tree intended for some children's museum? One would say so.

The little ones group themselves round me; they look at the treasure-trove with longing eyes; they would like to add it to the contents of their toy-box. It is much prettier in shape than an agate marble, much more graceful than an ivory egg or a boxwood top. The material, it is true, seems none too nicely chosen; but it is firm to the touch and very artistically curved. In any case, the little pear discovered underground must not go to swell the nursery collection until we have found out more about it.

Can it really be the Sacred Beetle's work? Is there an egg inside it, a grub? The shepherd assures me that there is. A similar pear, crushed by accident in the digging, contained, he says, a white egg, the size of a grain of wheat. I dare not believe it, so greatly does the object which he has brought me differ from the ball which I expected to see.

To open the mysterious prize and ascertain its contents would perhaps be imprudent: such an act of violence might jeopardize the life of the germ within, always provided that the Scarab's egg be there, a matter of which the shepherd seems convinced. Besides, I say to myself, the pear-shape, so totally opposed to all our accepted ideas, is probably accidental. Who knows if luck will ever give me anything like it again? I should be wise to keep the thing just as it is and await events; above all, I should be wise to go and seek for information on the spot.

The shepherd was at his post by daybreak the next morning. I joined him on some slopes that had been lately cleared of their trees, where the hot summer sun, which strikes with such force on the back of one's neck, could not reach us for two or three hours. In the cool morning air, with the Sheep browsing under Sultan's care, the two of us scattered on our search.

A Sacred Beetle's burrow is soon found: you can tell it by the fresh little mound of earth above it. With a vigorous turn of the wrist, my companion digs away with the little pocket-trowel which I have lent him. Incorrigible earth-scraper that I am, I seldom set forth without this light but serviceable tool. While he digs, I lie down, the better to see the arrangement and furniture of the cellar which we are unearthing, and I am all eyes. The shepherd uses the trowel as a lever and, with his other hand, holds back and pushes aside the soil.

Here we are! A cave opens out and, in the moist warmth of the yawning vault, I see a splendid pear lying full length upon the ground. No, I shall not soon forget this first revelation of the Scarab's maternal masterpiece. My excitement could have been no greater had I been an archæologist digging among the ancient relics of Egypt and lighting upon the sacred insect of the dead, carved in emerald, in some Pharaonic crypt. O ineffable moment, when truth suddenly shines forth! What other joys can compare with that holy rapture! The shepherd was in the seventh heaven; he laughed in response to my smile and was happy in my gladness.

Luck does not repeat itself: '*Non bis in idem,*' says the old adage. And here have I twice had under my eyes this curious pear-shape. Is it by any chance the normal shape, not subject to exception? Must we abandon the thought of a sphere similar to those which the insect rolls along the ground? Let us continue and we shall see.

A second hole is found. Like the previous one, it contains a pear. My two treasures are as like as two peas; they might have issued from the same mould. And here is a valuable confirmatory detail: in the second burrow, by the side of the pear and fondly embracing it, is the mother Beetle, engaged no doubt in giving it the finishing touches before leaving the underground cave for good. All doubts are dispelled: I know the worker and I know the work.

The rest of the morning provided abundant corroboration of these premisses: before an intolerable sun drove me from the slope which I was exploring, I was in possession of a dozen pears identical in shape and almost in dimensions. On several occasions the mother was present in the workshop.

To conclude this part of our subject, let me tell what the future held in store for me. All through the dog-days, from the end of June until September,

I paid almost daily visits to the spots frequented by the Sacred Beetle; and the burrows unearthed by my trowel furnished an amount of evidence exceeding my fondest hopes. The insects reared in captivity supplied me with more facts, though these, it is true, were very scanty in comparison with the rich crop from the open fields. All told, about a hundred nests, at the lowest computation, passed through my hands; and they were invariably the graceful pear-shape, never, absolutely never, the round shape of the pill, never the ball of which the books tell us.

I myself once shared this error, placing as I did implicit confidence in the words of the learned authorities. My old hunting-expeditions on the Plateau des Angles led to no result; my attempts at home-rearing failed pitifully; and yet I was anxious to give my young readers some idea of the nest built by the Sacred Beetle. I therefore adopted the traditional theory of the round shape; and then, taking analogy for my guide, I made use of the little that I had learnt from other dung-rollers to attempt an approximate sketch of the Sacred Beetle's work. It was an unlucky shot. Analogy no doubt is a valuable servant, but oh, how poor compared with direct observation! Deceived by this guide, so often untrustworthy amid the inexhaustible variety of life, I helped to perpetuate the blunder; and so I hasten to apologize, begging the reader to dismiss from his mind the little that I have said heretofore on the probable nest-building methods of the Sacred Beetle.

And now let us unfold the authentic story, admitting as evidence only facts actually observed again and again. The Sacred Beetle's nest is betrayed on the outside by a little heap of earth, by a tiny mound formed of the superfluous soil which the mother, when closing up the abode, has been unable to replace, part of the excavation having to be left empty. Under this mound is a shaft which is rarely more than four inches in depth, followed by a horizontal gallery, either straight or winding, which ends in a spacious hall, large enough to contain a man's fist. This is the crypt in which the egg lies enveloped in food and subjected to the incubation of a hot sun baking the ground only a few inches above it; this is the roomy workshop in which the mother, unfettered in her movements, has kneaded and shaped the future nurseling's food into a pear.

This stercoraceous bread has its main axis lying in a horizontal position. Its shape and size remind one exactly of those little Midsummer's Day pears which, by virtue of their bright colouring, their flavour and their early ripening, are so popular with the children. There is a slight variation in the bulk of the pears found. The largest dimensions are 45 millimetres in length by 30 millimetres in width;1 the smallest are 35 millimetres by 28.2

Without being as polished as stucco, the surface, which is absolutely even, is carefully glazed with a thin layer of red earth. At first soft as potter's clay, the pyriform loaf soon dries and acquires a stout crust which refuses to yield to the pressure of the fingers. Wood itself is no harder. This rind is the defensive wrapper that isolates the recluse from the world and allows him to consume his victuals in profound peace. But, should the central mass become dried up, then the danger is extremely serious. We shall have occasion to refer to the unhappy lot of the grub condemned to a diet of too stale bread.

What dough does the Scarab's bakehouse use? Who are the purveyors? The Horse and the Mule? By no means. Yet that was what I expected—and so would anybody—after seeing the insect make such energetic raids, for its own use, upon the overflowing store of an ordinary lump of dung. That is where it habitually manufactures the rolling ball which it goes and consumes in some underground retreat.

While coarse bread, full of bits of hay, is good enough for the mother, she becomes more particular where her children are concerned. She now wants the very daintiest pastry, rich in nourishment and easily digested; she wants the ovine manna: not that which the Sheep of a costive habit scatters in trails of black olives, but that which, elaborated in a less dry intestine, is fashioned into a single flat cake. This is the material required, the dough exclusively used. It is no longer the poor and stringy produce of the Horse, but an unctuous, plastic, homogeneous thing, soaked through and through with nutritive juices. Its plasticity and delicacy make it an admirable medium for an artistic piece of work like the Scarab's pear, while its alimentary qualities suit the weak stomach of the new-born grub. There may not be much of it, but the infant Beetle will find it sufficient for his needs.

This explains the smallness of these pears, a point which made me suspicious of the origin of my treasure until I found the mother present with the provisions. I was unable to see in those little pears the bill of fare of a future Sacred Beetle, who is so great a glutton and of so remarkable a size.

It probably also explains my failure in the old days with my cages. In my profound ignorance of the Sacred Beetle's domestic life, I used to supply her with what I could pick up here and there, droppings of Horse or Mule; and the Beetle refused it for her children and declined to build a nest. To-day, taught by my experience in the fields, I go to the Sheep for my supplies and all is well in the cages. Does this mean that the insect never employs for its breeding-pears materials derived from the Horse, even if selected from the finest strata and carefully cleansed from objectionable matter? If the best cannot be obtained, is the middling refused? I prefer to be cautious and give no opinion. What I can declare is that I inspected over a hundred burrows with a view to writing this story, and that in every case, from first to last, the larva's provisions had been obtained from the Sheep.

Where is the egg in that nutritive mass so novel in shape? One would be inclined to place it in the centre of the fat, round paunch. This central point is best protected against accidents from the outside, best off in the matter of temperature. Besides, the nascent grub would here find a deep layer of food on every side of it and would not be liable to make mistakes in the first mouthfuls. Everything being of the same kind all round it, there would be no necessity for it to pick and choose; wherever it chanced to apply its prentice tooth, it could continue without hesitation its first dainty repast.

All this sounds so very rational that I allowed myself to be led away by it. In the first pear that I examined, layer by layer, shaving off slices with my penknife, I looked for the egg in the centre of the paunch, feeling almost certain of finding it there. To my great surprise, it was not there. Instead of being hollow, the centre of the pear is full and consists of one continuous uniform alimentary mass.

My deductions, which any observer in my place would certainly have shared, seemed very reasonable; the Scarab, however, is of another way of thinking. We have our logic, of which we are rather proud; the dung-kneader has hers, which is better than ours in this instance. She has her own foresight, takes her own precautions; and she places the egg elsewhere.

But where? Why, in the narrow part of the pear, in the neck, right at the end! Let us cut this neck lengthwise, taking the necessary precautions not to damage the contents. It is hollowed into a niche with polished and shiny walls. This niche is the tabernacle of the germ, the hatching-chamber. The egg, which is very large in proportion to the size of the mother, is an elongated oval, about ten millimetres in length with a diameter of five millimetres at the widest part.3 It is white and is separated on all sides from the walls of the chamber by a slight empty space, the only contact being at the rear end of the egg, which adheres to the top of the niche. Lying horizontally, in conformity with the normal position of the pear, the whole of it, excepting the point of attachment, thus rests upon an air-mattress, warmest and most buoyant of beds.

Now we know all about it. Let us next try to understand the Scarab's logic. Let us find out why she has to make that pear of hers, so unusual a shape in insect structures; let us seek to explain the suitability of the egg's curious position. We are venturing on dangerous ground when we enquire into the how and wherefore of things. We easily lose our footing in that mysterious land where the moving soil gives way beneath us, swallowing the foolhardy in the quicksands of error. Must we abandon such excursions, because of the risk? Why should we?

What does our science, so sublime compared with the feebleness of our resources, so contemptible in the face of the boundless stretches of the unknown, what does it know of absolute reality? Nothing. The world interests us only because of the ideas which we form of it. Remove the idea and everything becomes a desert, chaos, nothingness. An omnium-gatherum of facts is not knowledge, but at most a cold catalogue which we must thaw and quicken at the fire of the mind; we must bring to it thought and the light of reason; we must interpret.

Let us adopt this course to explain the work of the Sacred Beetle. Perhaps we shall end by attributing our own logic to the insect. After all, it will be just as remarkable to see a wonderful agreement prevail between that which reason dictates to us and that which instinct dictates to the insect.

A grave danger threatens the Sacred Beetle in his grub state: the drying-up of the food. The crypt in which the larval life is spent has a layer of earth, some four inches thick, for a ceiling. Of what avail is this flimsy screen against the torrid heat that beats down upon the soil, baking it like a brick to a far greater depth than that? At times the temperature of the grub's abode mounts towards boiling-point; when I thrust my hand into it, I feel the hot air of a Turkish bath.

The provisions, therefore, even though they have to last but three or four weeks, are liable to dry up before that time and to become uneatable. When, instead of the soft bread of its first meal, the unhappy grub finds nothing to stay its stomach but a horrible crust, hard as a pebble and tooth-proof, it is bound to perish of hunger. And it does actually so perish. I have found numbers of these victims of the August sun which, after eating plentifully of the fresh food and digging themselves a cell in it, had succumbed, unable to continue biting into provisions that had become too hard. There remained a thick shell, a sort of closed oven, in which the poor thing lay baked and shrivelled up.

While the grub dies of hunger in a shell which has dried into stone, the full-grown insect that has completed its transformations dies there too, for it is incapable of bursting the prison and freeing itself. I shall come back later to the question of the final emergence and will say no more about it for the present. Let us confine our attention to the troubles of the grub.

The drying-up of the victuals is, I have said, fatal to it. This is proved by the larvæ found baked in their oven; it is also proved, in a more definite fashion, by the following experiment. In July, the period of active nidification, I place in wooden or cardboard boxes a dozen pears unearthed that morning from their native burrows. These boxes, carefully closed, are put away in the dark, in my study, where the same temperature prevails as outside. Well, in none of them is the infant reared: sometimes the egg shrivels; sometimes the worm is hatched, but very soon dies. On the other hand, in tin boxes or glass receptacles, everything goes well: not one attempt at rearing fails.

Whence do these differences arise? Simply from this: in the high temperature of July, evaporation proceeds apace under the permeable wooden or cardboard screen; the food-pear dries up; and the unfortunate worm dies of hunger. In the impermeable tin boxes, in the carefully-sealed glass receptacles, there is no evaporation; the provisions retain their softness; and the grubs thrive as well as in their native burrow.

The insect employs two methods to ward off the danger of desiccation. In the first place, it compresses the outer layer with all the strength of its stout, flat fore-arms, turning it into a protective rind more homogeneous and more compact than the central mass. If I break one of these dried-up provision-boxes, the rind usually comes clean away, leaving the centre part bare. The whole suggests the shell and kernel of a nut. The pressure exercised by the mother when manipulating her pear has affected the surface layer to a depth of a few millimetres, and this has produced the rind; the influence of the pressure is not felt lower down, and the result is the big central kernel. In the hot summer months, the housewife puts her bread into a closed pan, to keep it fresh. This is what the insect does, in its fashion: by dint of compression, it covers the family bread with a pan.

The Sacred Beetle does not stop there: she becomes a geometrician capable of solving a delicate problem of minimum values. Other conditions being equal, evaporation obviously takes place in proportion to the extent of the evaporating surface. The alimentary mass must therefore be given the smallest possible surface, in order to reduce the waste of moisture as much as possible; at the same time, this minimum surface must incorporate the maximum aggregate of nutritive materials, so that the grub may find sufficient nourishment. Now what is the form that encloses the greatest bulk within the smallest superficial area? Geometry answers, the sphere.

The Scarab, therefore, shapes the larva's ration into a sphere (we will leave the neck of the pear out of the question for the moment); and this round form is not the result of blind mechanical conditions, imposing an inevitable shape upon the worker; it is not the violent effect of the rolling along the ground. We have already seen that, for the purpose of easier and swifter transit, the insect kneads into a perfect sphere the materials which it intends to consume at a distance, without moving that sphere from the spot on which it rests; in short, we have realized that the round form precedes the rolling.

In the same way, it will be seen presently that the pear destined for the grub is fashioned in the burrow. It undergoes no rolling-process, it is not even moved. The Sacred Beetle gives it the requisite outline exactly as a modelling artist might do, shaping his clay under the pressure of his thumb.

With the tools which it possesses, the insect could obtain other forms of a less delicate curve than its pear-shaped piece of work. It could, for instance, make a rough cylinder, the sausage customary among the Geotrupes; or, simplifying the work to the utmost, it could leave the lump without any definite form, just as it happened to find it. Things would proceed all the faster and would leave more time for playing in the sun. But no: the Sacred Beetle never chooses any shape but the sphere, though it necessitates such scrupulous accuracy; she acts as though she knew the laws of evaporation and geometry from beginning to end.

It remains for us to examine the neck of the pear. What can be its object, its use? The reply forces itself upon us irresistibly. This neck contains the egg, in the hatching-chamber. Now every germ, whether of plant or animal, needs air, the primary stimulus of life. To admit that vivifying combustible, the shell of a bird's egg is riddled with an endless number of pores. The pear of the Sacred Beetle may be compared with the egg of the Hen. Its shell is the rind, hardened by pressure, to avoid untimely desiccation; its nutritive mass, its meat, its yolk is the soft ball sheltered under the rind; its air-chamber is the terminal space, the cavity in the neck, where the air envelops the germ on every side. Where would that germ be better off, for breathing, than in its hatching-chamber projecting into the atmosphere and giving free play to the passage of gases through its thin and easily permeable wall?

In the centre of the mass, on the other hand, aeration is not so easy. The hardened rind does not possess pores like an egg-shell's; and the central kernel is formed of compact matter. The air enters it nevertheless, for presently the grub will be able to live in it: the grub, a robust organism which does not need the same tender flutter of life as the sensitive germ.

Where the adolescent larva thrives, the egg would die of suffocation. Here is a proof of it. I take a small, wide-necked phial and fill it with Sheep-dung, the fare required in this case. I push in a bit of stick and obtain a shaft which shall represent the hatching-chamber. Down this shaft I place an egg carefully moved from its cell. I close the orifice and cover up everything with a thickly-heaped layer of the same material. Here, in all excepting the shape, we have an artificial reproduction of the Sacred Beetle's pellet; only, in this instance, the egg is in the centre of the mass, the place which over-hasty considerations made us but now believe the most suitable. Well, the point which we selected is fatal to life. The egg dies there. What has it lacked? Apparently, proper aeration.

Plenteously enveloped by the clammy mass, which is a bad conductor of heat, it is also deprived of the mild temperature needed for its hatching. In addition to air, every germ requires heat. In order to be as near as possible to the incubator, the germ in the bird's egg is on the surface of the yolk and, thanks to its extreme mobility, always comes to the top, no matter what the position of the egg may be. Thus the most is made of the maternal heating-apparatus seated upon the brood.

In the insect's case, the incubator is the earth, which is warmed by the sun. Its germ likewise comes close to the heating-apparatus; it goes as near as it can to the universal incubator, in search of its spark of life; instead of remaining sunk in the middle of the inert mass, it takes up its position at the top of a projecting nipple, lapped on all sides by the warm emanations of the soil.

These conditions, air and warmth, are so fundamental that no Dung-beetle neglects them. The piles of food hoarded vary in form, as we shall have an opportunity of seeing: in addition to the pear, such shapes as the cylinder, the ovoid, the pill and the thimble are adopted, according to the genus of the manipulator; but, amid this diversity of outline, one primary feature remains unchanged, and that is the placing of the egg in a hatching-chamber close to the surface which allows free access to air and heat. And the most gifted in this delicate art of knowing just where to place the egg is the Sacred Beetle with her pear.

I was saying just now that this foremost of dung-kneaders behaved with a logic that rivals our own. By this time, my statement has been completely established. Here is something better still. Let us submit the following problem to our leading scientific lights: a germ is accompanied by a mass of victuals liable soon to be rendered useless by desiccation. How should the alimentary mass be shaped? Where should the egg be laid so as to be easily influenced by air and heat?

The first question of the problem has already been answered. Knowing that evaporation varies in proportion to the extent of the evaporating surface, science declares that the victuals shall be arranged in the form of a ball, because the spherical shape is that which encloses the greatest amount of material within the smallest surface. As for the egg, since it requires a protecting sheath to keep it from any harmful contact, it shall be contained within a thin, cylindrical case; and this case shall be fixed upon the sphere.

Thus the requisite conditions are fulfilled: the provisions, packed into a ball, keep fresh; the egg, protected by its slender, cylindrical sheath, receives the influence of warmth and air without impediment. The strictly needful has been obtained; but it is very ugly. Utility has paid no attention to beauty.

An artist corrects the crude work of reason. He replaces the cylinder by a semi-ellipsoid, so much prettier in form; he joins this ellipsoid to the sphere by means of a graceful curved surface; and the whole becomes the pear, the necked gourd. It is now a work of art, a thing of beauty.

The Sacred Beetle does exactly what æsthetic considerations dictate to ourselves. Can she, too, have a sense of beauty? Is she able to appreciate the elegance of her pear? True, she does not see it: she manipulates it in profound darkness. But she touches it. A poor touch hers, roughly clad in horn, yet not insensible, after all, to delicate contours.

It occurred to me to put children's intelligence to the test with this problem in æsthetics suggested by the Sacred Beetle's work. I wanted very immature minds, hardly opened, still slumbering in the misty clouds of early childhood, in short, approximating as nearly as possible to the vague intellect of the insect, if any such approximation is permissible. At the same time I wanted them to be clear-headed enough to understand me. I selected some untutored youngsters, of whom the oldest was six.

I submitted to this tribunal the work of the Sacred Beetle and a geometrical production of my own fingers, representing in the same dimensions the sphere surmounted by a short cylinder. Taking each of them aside, as though for confession, lest the opinion of one should influence the opinion of another, I sprang my two toys upon them and asked them which they thought the prettier. There were five of them; and they all voted for the Sacred Beetle's pear.

I was struck by this unanimity. The rough little peasant-lad, who has scarcely yet learnt how to blow his nose, has already a certain sense of elegance of form. He can distinguish between the beautiful and the ugly. Can this be also true of the Sacred Beetle? No one who knew what he was talking about would venture to say yes; no one either would venture to say no. It is a question that cannot be answered, since we cannot consult the one and only judge in this case. After all, the solution might very well be exceedingly simple. What does the flower know of its glorious corolla? What does the snowflake know of its exquisite hexagonal stars? Like the flower and the snowflake, the Sacred Beetle might well be ignorant of the beautiful, though it be her work.

There is beauty everywhere, on the express condition that there be an eye capable of recognizing it. Is this eye of the mind, this eye which appraises correctness of form, to some extent an attribute of the dumb creation? If the Toad's ideal of beauty is unquestionably the She-toad, outside the irresistible attraction of the sexes is there really such a thing as beauty to an animal? Considered generally, what is beauty, actually? Beauty is order. What is order? Harmony in the whole design. What is harmony? Harmony is.... But enough. Answers would follow upon questions without ever touching the real principle of it all, the immovable foundation. What a lot of philosophizing over a lump of dung! It is high time to change the subject.

1 1·75 × 1·17 inches.—*Translator's Note.*

2 1·36 × 1·09 inches.—*Translator's Note.*

3 ·39 × ·19 inch.—*Translator's Note.*

CHAPTER V
THE SACRED BEETLE: THE MODELLING

Here we are on solid ground, in the domain of facts, of things that can be seen and recorded. How does the Sacred Beetle obtain the maternal pear? To begin with, it is certain that this shape is not achieved by the process of transport, for it is not at all what one would get from haphazard rolling in all directions. The belly of the gourd might be made in that way; but the neck, the elliptical nipple hollowed into a hatching-chamber: that delicate work could never result from a series of violent, irregular bumps. A goldsmith does not hammer out a jewel on a blacksmith's anvil! Together with other sound reasons already adduced, the pear-shaped outline delivers us, I hope, once and for all, from the antiquated belief that the egg has its home inside a roughly-jolted sphere.

To produce his masterpiece, the sculptor retires to his den. Even so the Sacred Beetle. She shuts herself in her crypt, with the materials which she has brought down there, in order to concentrate upon her modelling. The block out of which she is to shape her pear may be obtained in two ways. Sometimes the Beetle manages to secure from the heap, by the method familiar to us, a fine mass of material which is kneaded into a ball on the spot and which is a perfect sphere before it is set in motion. Were it only a question of provisions intended for her own meal, she would never act otherwise.

When the ball is deemed big enough, if the place does not suit her wherein to dig the burrow, she sets out with her rolling burden, going at random till she lights upon a favourable spot. On the way, the ball, without becoming any rounder than it was to start with, hardens a little on the surface and is encrusted with earth and tiny grains of sand. This earthy rind, picked up on the road, is an authentic sign of a more or less long journey. The detail is not without importance; we shall find it useful presently.

At other times, the Beetle may hit upon a suitable site for her burrow close to the heap which has provided her block. The soil may be free from pebbles and easy to dig. In that case there is no need of any travelling, and consequently no need to make a ball. The soft droppings of the Sheep are gathered and stored as found, entering the workshop as a shapeless mass, either in one lump or, if need be, in several.

This rarely happens under natural conditions, because of the roughness of the ground, which is full of stones and flints. Sites practicable for easy digging are few and far between; and the insect has to roam about, with its burden, to find them. In my cages, on the other hand, where the layer of earth has been passed through a sieve, it is the usual case. Here the soil is easy to dig at any point; and so the mother, who is anxious to get her eggs laid, merely lowers the nearest lump underground, without waiting to give it any definite form.

Whether this storing without any preliminary modelling or carting take place in the fields or in my cages, the ultimate result is most striking. One day, I see a shapeless lump disappear into the crypt. Next day, or the day after, I visit the workshop and find the artist in front of her work. The original formless mass, the armfuls of scrapings carried down, have become a pear perfect in outline and exquisitely finished.

The artistic object bears the marks of its method of manufacture. The part that rests upon the bottom of the cavity is crusted over with earthy particles; all the rest is of a glossy polish. Owing to its weight, owing also to the pressure exercised when the Beetle manipulated it, the pear, while still quite soft, became soiled with grains of earth on the side that touched the floor of the workshop; on the remainder, which is the larger part, it has retained the delicate finish which the insect was able to give it.

The inferences to be drawn from these carefully noted details are obvious: the pear is no turner's work; it has not been obtained by any sort of rolling on the ground of the spacious studio, for in that case it would have been soiled with earth all over. Besides, its projecting neck eliminates this method of fabrication. And its unblemished upper surface is eloquent testimony that it has not even been turned from one side to the other. The Beetle, therefore, has moulded it where it lies, without turning or shifting it at all; she has modelled it with little taps of her broad paddles, just as we saw her model her ball in the daylight.

Let us now return to what usually happens in the free state. The materials then come from a distance and are carried into the burrow in the form of a ball covered with soil on every part of its surface. What will the insect do with this sphere which contains the paunch of the future pear ready-made? It would be easy to answer this if I concerned myself only with results, without troubling how those results were obtained. It would be enough for me, as I have often done, to capture the mother in her burrow with her ball and take the whole lot home, to my insect laboratory, in order to keep a close watch on events.

I fill a large glass jar with earth, sifted, moistened and heaped to the desired depth. I place the mother and the beloved pill which she is clasping on the surface of this artificial soil. I stow away the apparatus in a dim corner and wait. My patience is not tried very long. Urged by the insistent ovaries, the Beetle resumes her interrupted work.

In certain cases, I see her, still on the surface, destroying her ball, ripping it up, cutting it to pieces, shredding it. This is not in the least the act of one in despair who, finding herself a captive, breaks the precious object in her madness. It is based on sound hygienics. A scrupulous inspection of the morsel which she has gathered in haste, among lawless competitors, is often necessary, for supervision is not always easy on the harvest-field itself, in the midst of thieves and robbers. The ball may be harbouring a collection of little Onthophagi and Aphodii who passed unnoticed in the heat of acquisition.

These involuntary intruders, finding themselves very well-off in the heart of the mass, would make good use of the future pear, much to the detriment of the legitimate consumer. The ball must be purged of this hungry brood. The mother, therefore, pulls it to pieces and scrutinizes the fragments closely. Then the sorted bits are carefully put together again and the ball remade, this time without any earthy rind. It is dragged underground and becomes an immaculate pear, always excepting the surface touching the soil.

Oftener still, the ball is thrust by the mother into the soil in the jar just as I took it from the burrow, still with the rough crust which it has acquired in its cross-country rolling from the place where it was obtained to the place where the insect intends to use it. In that event, I find it at the bottom of my jar transformed into a pear, but still rough and encrusted with earth and sand over the whole of its surface, thus proving that the pear-shaped outline has not demanded a general recasting of the mass, inside as well as out, but has been obtained by simple pressure and by drawing out the neck.

This is how, in the vast majority of cases, things happen under normal conditions. Almost all the pears that I dig up in the fields have rinds and are unpolished, some more, others less. If we put on one side the inevitable incrustations due to the carting-process, these blemishes would seem to point to a prolonged rolling in the interior of the subterranean manor. The few which I find perfectly smooth, especially those wonderfully neat specimens furnished by my cages, dispel this mistake entirely. They show us that, when the materials are collected near the burrow and stored away unshaped, the pear is modelled wholly without rolling; they prove to us that, in other cases, the lines of earth and grit on the outside of the ball are not a sign of its having been rolled to and fro in the workshop, but are simply the marks of a fairly long journey on the surface of the ground.

To be present at the construction of the pear is no easy matter: the mystery-loving artist obstinately refuses to do any work as soon as the light reaches her. She needs absolute darkness for her modelling; and I need light if I would see her at her task. It is impossible to unite the two conditions. Let us try, nevertheless; let us catch some glimpses of the truth whose fulness eludes our vision.

The arrangements made are as follows: I once more take the big jar. I cover the bottom with a layer of earth two or three inches deep. To obtain the transparent workshop necessary for my observations, I fix a tripod on the earthy layer and, on this support, about four inches in height, I place a round piece of deal of the same diameter as the jar. The glass-walled chamber thus marked out will represent the roomy crypt in which the insect works. A piece is scolloped out of the edge of the deal block, large enough to permit of the passage of the Beetle and her ball. Lastly, above this screen, I heap a layer of earth as deep as the jar allows.

During the operation, a portion of the upper earth falls through the opening and slips down to the lower space in a wide inclined plane. This was a circumstance which I had foreseen and which was indispensable to my plan. By means of this slope, the artist, when she has found the communicating trap-door, will make for the transparent cell which I have arranged for her. She will make for it, of course, only provided that she be in perfect darkness. I therefore make a cardboard cylinder, closed at the top, and place it over the glass jar. Left standing where it is, the opaque sheath will provide the dusk which the insect wants; suddenly raised, it will give the light which I want.

Things being thus arranged, I go in quest of a mother who has just withdrawn into solitude with her ball. A morning's search is enough to provide me with what I need. I place the mother and her ball on the surface of the upper layer of earth; I cap the apparatus with its cardboard sheath; and I wait. I say to myself that the Beetle is too persevering to give up work until her egg is housed and that she will therefore dig herself a new burrow, dragging her ball with her as she goes; she will pass through the upper layer of earth, which is not sufficiently thick; she will come upon the deal board, an obstacle similar to the broken stones that often bar her passage in the course of her normal excavations; she will investigate the cause of the impediment and, finding the opening, will descend through this trap-door to the lower compartment, which, being free and roomy, will represent to the insect the crypt whence I have just removed it. But all this takes time; and I must wait for the morrow to satisfy my impatient curiosity.

The hour has come: let us go and see. The study-door was left open yesterday: the mere sound of the door-handle might disturb and stop my distrustful worker. By way of greater precaution, before entering I put on noiseless slippers. And now, whoosh! The cylinder is removed. Capital! My forecast was correct.

The Beetle occupies the glazed studio. I surprise her at work, with her broad foot laid on the rough model of the pear. But, startled by the sudden light, she remains motionless, as though petrified. This lasts a few seconds. Then she turns her back upon me and awkwardly ascends the inclined plane, to reach the dim heights of her gallery. I give a glance at the work, take note of its shape and its position, and once more restore darkness with the cardboard sheath. Let us not prolong our intrusion, if we would renew the test.

My sudden, short visit gives us some idea of the mysterious work. The ball, which at first was absolutely spherical, is now depressed at the top into a sort of shallow crater with a swollen rim. The thing reminds me, on a very much smaller scale, of certain prehistoric pots, with a round belly, a thick-lipped mouth and a narrow groove round the neck. This rough model of the future pear tells us of the insect's method, a method identical with that of pleistocene man ignorant of the potter's wheel.

The plastic ball, ringed at one end, has had a groove made in it, the starting-point of the neck of the pear; it has also been drawn out slightly into a rather blunt projection. In the centre of this projection pressure has been applied. The first stage of the work therefore consists merely in placing a ring round the ball and applying pressure.

Towards evening I pay another sudden visit, in complete silence. The insect has recovered from its excitement of the morning and gone down again to its workshop. Troubled by the flood of light, baffled by the strange events to which my artifices give rise, it at once makes off and takes refuge in the upper story. The poor mother, persecuted by these illuminations, moves away into the darkest recesses; but she goes regretfully, with hesitating steps.

The work has progressed. The crater has become deeper; its thick lips have disappeared, are thinner, closer together, drawn out into the neck of a pear. The object, however, has not changed its place. Its position and direction are exactly as I noted them before. The side that rested on the ground is still at the bottom, at the same point; the side that faced upwards is still at the top; the crater that lay on my right has been replaced by the neck, still on my right. All of which gives conclusive proof of my earlier statements: there is no rolling, but only pressure, which kneads and shapes.

The next day, a third visit. The pear is finished. Its neck, yesterday a yawning sack, is now closed. The egg, therefore, is laid; the work is completed and demands only the finishing touches of general polishing, touches upon which the mother, so intent on geometrical perfection, was doubtless engaged at the time when I disturbed her.

The most delicate part of the business escapes my observation. Roughly speaking, I can see plainly how the egg's hatching-chamber is obtained: the thick pad surrounding the original crater is thinned and flattened under the pressure of the feet and is lengthened into a sack the mouth of which gradually narrows. Up to this point the work provides its own explanation. But, when we think of the insect's rigid tools, its broad, toothed fore-arms, whose spasmodic movements remind us of the stiff gestures of an automaton, we are left without any explanation of the exquisite perfection of the cell which is to be the hatching-chamber of the egg.

With this crude equipment, excellently adapted to pickaxe-work though it be, how does the Scarab obtain the natal dwelling, the oval nest so daintily polished and glazed within? Does her foot, a regular saw, fitted with enormous teeth, begin to rival the artist's brush in delicacy from the moment when it is inserted through the narrow orifice of the sack? Why not? I have said elsewhere, and this is the moment to say it again: the tool does not make the workman. The insect exercises its own particular talents with any kind of tool with which it is supplied. It can saw with a plane or plane with a saw, like the model workman of whom Franklin tells us. The same strong-toothed rake which the Sacred Beetle uses to open up the earth she also employs as a trowel and brush wherewith to glaze the stucco of the chamber in which the grub will be born.

In conclusion, one more detail concerning this hatching-chamber. At the extreme end of the neck of the pear, one point is always pretty clearly distinguished: it bristles with stringy fibres, while the rest of the neck is carefully polished. This is the plug with which the mother has closed the narrow opening after carefully depositing the egg; and this plug, as its hairy structure shows, has not been subjected to the pressure exerted over all the rest of the mass, working into it any projecting bits, however small, till not the slightest sign of roughness remains.

Why does the extreme end of the pear receive this special treatment, a most curious exception, when nothing else has eluded the heavy blows of the insect's legs? The reason is that the hind-end of the egg rests against this plug, which, were it pressed down and driven in, would transmit the pressure to the germ and imperil its safety. So the mother, aware of the risk, stops the hole without ramming down the stopper: the air in the hatching-chamber is thus more easily renewed; and the egg escapes the dangerous activity of the powerful rammer.

CHAPTER VI
THE SACRED BEETLE: THE LARVA

Under the thin ceiling of the burrow, the Sacred Beetle's egg undergoes the varying influences of the sun, the supreme incubator. Consequently there is not, nor can there be, any fixed date for the quickening of the germ. In very hot, sunny weather, I have obtained a grub five or six days after the egg was laid; with a more moderate temperature, I have had to wait until the twelfth day. June and July are the hatching-months.

As soon as the new-born grub has flung aside its swaddling clothes, it forthwith bites into the walls of its chamber. If starts eating its house, not anyhow, but with unerring wisdom. If it nibbled at the thin side of its cell—and there is nothing to dissuade it, for here as elsewhere the materials are of excellent quality—if its mandibles scraped the extreme end of the nipple, the weakest point, it would make a breach in the protecting wall before it had sufficient putty to repair that breach. This putty is the material which we shall see the larva using later, when accidents of that kind occur from external causes.

If it ate into its heap of provisions at random, it would expose itself to serious risks from the outside; at the very least it would be liable to slip out of its cradle and tumble to the ground through the open window. Once it falls out of its cell, there is no hope for the little grub. It will not know how to make its way back to the larder; and, if it does find its heap of provisions again, it will be repelled by the hard rind with its bits of grit and sand. In its wisdom, greater than any possessed by the young of the higher animals, which are always watched over by a mother, the new-born larva, still sleek and shiny with the slime of the egg, thoroughly knows the danger and avoids it by masterly tactics.

Though all the food around it is alike and all is to its taste, nevertheless it tackles exclusively the floor of its cell, a floor continued by the bulky sphere in which bites will be permissible in every direction, as the consumer pleases.

Can any one explain why this particular spot is chosen as the starting-point, when there is nothing to distinguish it, from the point of view of food? Could the tiny creature be warned of the proximity of the outer air by the effect which a thin wall has on its sensitive skin? If so, how is this effect produced? Besides, what does a grub, that moment born, know of outside dangers? I am quite in the dark.

Or rather I begin to see daylight. I recognize once again, under another aspect, what was taught me some years ago by the Scolia-wasps1 and the Sphex-wasps,2 those scientific eaters, those skilful anatomists, who can discriminate so well between the lawful and the unlawful and are consequently able to devour their prey without killing it until the end of the meal. The Sacred Beetle has his own complicated art of eating. Though he need not trouble about the preservation of the victuals, which are not liable to go bad, he has nevertheless to guard against ill-timed mouthfuls, which would rob him of his shelter. Of these dangerous mouthfuls, the earliest are the most to be feared, because of the creature's weakness and the thinness of the wall. As its protection, therefore, the grub has, in its own way, the primal inspiration without which none would be able to live; it obeys the imperious voice of instinct, which says:

'There shalt thou bite and no elsewhere.'

And, respecting all the rest, however tempting, it bites at the prescribed spot; it eats into the pear at the bottom of the neck. In a few days it has worked its way deep down into the mass, where it waxes big and fat, transforming the filthy material into a plump larva gleaming with health, ivory-white with slate-coloured reflections and without a speck of dirt upon it. The matter which has disappeared, or rather which has been remelted in life's crucible, leaves empty a round cell into which the grub fits itself, curving its back under the spherical dome and bending double.

The time has come for a sight stranger than any yet displayed to me by the industrial prowess of an insect. Anxious to observe the grub in the intimacy of its home, I open in the belly of the pear a little peep-hole half a centimetre3 square. The head of the recluse at once appears in the opening, to enquire what is happening. The breach is perceived. The head disappears. I can just see the white back turning about in the narrow cabin; and, then and there, the window which I have made is closed with a soft, brown paste, which soon hardens.

The inside of the cabin, said I to myself, is no doubt a semifluid porridge. Turning round, as is shown by the sudden slide of its back, the grub has collected a handful of this material and, completing the circuit, has stuck its load, by way of mortar, in the breach which it considered dangerous. I remove the plug. The grub acts as before, puts its head at the window, withdraws it, spins round as easily as a nut in its shell and forthwith produces a second plug as ample as the first. Forewarned of what was coming, this time I saw more clearly.

What a mistake I had made! However, I am not so much startled as I might be: in the art of defence, animals often employ means which our imagination would not dare to contemplate. It is not the grub's head that is presented at the breach, after the preliminary twisting: it is the other extremity. It does not bring a lump of its alimentary dough, gathered by scraping the walls: it excretes upon the aperture to be closed, which is a much more economical proceeding. Sparingly measured out, the rations must not be wasted: there is just enough to live upon. Besides, the cement is of better quality; it soon sets. Lastly, the urgent repairs are more quickly effected if the intestines lend their kindly aid.

They do, in point of fact, and to an astonishing degree. Five, six times in succession and oftener, I remove the plug; and, time after time, the mortar ejects a copious discharge from its apparently inexhaustible reservoir, which is ever at the mason's service, without an interval for rest. The grub is already beginning to resemble the Sacred Beetle, whose stercoraceous prowess we know: it is a past master in the art of dunging. It possesses above any other animal in the world an intestinal docility which anatomy presently will undertake to explain to us in part.

The plasterer and the mason have their trowels. In the same way, the grub, that zealous repairer of breaches made in its home, has a trowel of its own. The last segment is lopped off slantwise and carries on its dorsal surface a sort of inclined plane, a broad disk surrounded by a fleshy pad. In the middle of the disk is a slit, forming the cementing-aperture. There you have your trowel, a most respectable one, flattened out and supplied with a rim to prevent the compressed matter from flowing away uselessly.

As soon as the mass of plastic matter has been emitted, the levelling- and compressing-instrument sets to work to introduce the cement well into the irregularities of the breach, to push it right through the thickness of the ruined portion, to give it consistency and smooth it. After this trowel-work, the grub turns round: it comes and finishes the job with its wide forehead and improves it with the tip of its mandibles. Wait a quarter of an hour; and the repaired portion will be as firm as the rest of the shell, so quickly does the cement set. Outside, the repairs are betrayed by the irregular projections where the stuff has been forced out, the part which the trowel could not reach; but, inside, there is no trace of the breakage: the usual polish has been restored at the damaged spot. A plasterer stopping a hole in one of our walls could produce no better piece of work.

Nor do the grub's talents end here. With its cement it becomes the mender of pots and pans. Let me explain. I have compared the outside of the pear, which, when pressed and dried, becomes a stout shell, with a jar containing fresh food. In the course of my excavations, sometimes made on difficult soil, I have happened occasionally to break this jar with an ill-directed blow of my trowel. I have collected the potsherds, pieced them together, after restoring the grub to its place, and kept the whole thing united by wrapping it in a scrap of newspaper.

On reaching home, I have found the pear put out of shape, no doubt, and seamed with scars, but just as solid as ever. During the walk, the grub had restored its ruined dwelling to condition. Cement injected into the cracks joined the pieces; inside, a thick plastering strengthened the inner wall, so much so that the repaired shell was quite as good as the untouched shell, except for the irregularity of the outside. In its artistically-mended stronghold the grub found the peace essential to its existence.

The time has come to ask ourselves the reason for this plasterer's craft. Destined to live in complete darkness, does the larva stop the cracks made in its house in order to avoid the unwelcome intrusion of the light? But it is blind. There is no trace of an organ of sight on its yellowish headpiece. The absence of eyes, however, does not authorize us to deny the influence of the light, an influence which perhaps is vaguely resented by the grub's delicate skin. Proofs are required. Here they are.

I manage to make my breach almost in the dark. The little light that remains is just sufficient to guide my house-breaking-implement. When the opening is made, I at once lower the shell into a dark box. A few minutes later, the hole is stopped. Despite the darkness in which it found itself, the grub has thought fit to seal up its cell.

In small jars packed full of provisions, I bring up larvæ taken from their native pear. A pit is dug in the mass of foodstuffs, ending at the bottom in a hemisphere. This cavity, representing about the half of the pear, will be the artificial cell given in exchange for the natural one. I put the grubs on which I am experimenting into separate cells. The change of residence produces no appreciable anxiety. Finding the food of my selecting very much to their taste, they bite into the walls with their customary appetite. Exile in no way perturbs those stoical stomachs; and my attempts at breeding are pursued unchecked.

A remarkable thing now happens. All my transplanted ones work little by little to complete the round nest of which my pit represented only the lower half. I have provided the flooring. They propose to add a ceiling, a dome, and thus to shut themselves up in a spherical enclosure. The materials are the putty supplied by the intestines; the building-tool is the trowel, the inclined plane of the final segment. Soft bricks are laid on the margin of the well. When these have set, they serve as a support for a second row, sloping slightly inwards. Other rows follow, marking the curve of the general structure more and more distinctly. Also, from time to time, a wriggle of the hinder part assists in determining the spherical conformation. In this way, without any supporting scaffold, without the cradle indispensable to our architects in building an arched roof, a commanding dome is obtained, built upon space and completing the sphere which I began.

Some of them shorten the work. The glass wall of the little jar occasionally comes within range. Its smooth surface suits the taste of these fastidious polishers; its curve, to a certain extent, coincides with that of their plan. They make use of it, doubtless not from economy of labour and time, but because, to their mind, the smooth round wall is a thing of their own making. In this way there is reserved, on the sides of the cupola, a large glazed window which answers my purpose admirably.

Well, the grubs which, all day long and for weeks on end, receive the bright light of my study through this window of mine keep as quiet as the others, eating and digesting, and never trouble to shut out any unwelcome rays with a blind made of their putty. We may take it therefore that, when the larva so eagerly closes the breach which I have made in its chamber, its object is not to protect itself from the light.

Does it fear draughts then, when it scrupulously fills up the least cranny through which the air might enter? This again is not the solution. The temperature is the same in my room and in the grub's; besides, when I perpetrate my burglaries, the atmosphere in my study is absolutely still. I do not examine the prisoner in a gale, but in the calm of my workroom, in the even profounder calm of a glass jar.

There can be no question of a cold breeze, which would be painful to a very sensitive skin; and nevertheless the air is the enemy to be avoided at all costs. If it flowed in at all plentifully through a breach, with the dryness which the July heat imparts to it, the provisions would be dried up. Faced with an uneatable biscuit, the grub would become languid and anæmic and would soon perish of hunger. The mother, to the best of her abilities, has guarded her offspring against death from starvation by making her pear round and giving it a stout rind; but, for all that, her children are not released from every obligation to watch their rations. If they want bread that keeps soft and fresh to the last, they must in their turn see to it that the provision-jar is properly closed. Crevices may appear, fraught with grave danger. It is important to stop them up without delay. This, if I be not utterly at fault, is the reason why the grub is a plasterer armed with a trowel and provided with a workshop that can always furnish plenty of putty. The pot-mender repairs his cracked jar in order to keep his bread nice and soft.

A serious objection suggests itself. The slits, the breaches, the vent-holes which I see so zealously cemented are the work of my instruments: tweezers, penknife, dissecting-needles. It cannot be maintained that the grub is endowed with its strange talent to protect itself against the troubles brought upon it by human curiosity. What has it to fear from man, in its life underground? Nothing, or next to nothing. Since the Sacred Beetle started rolling his ball under the broad canopy of the sky, I am probably the first to worry his family in order to make them talk to me and instruct me. Others will come after me perhaps; but they will be very few! No, man's destructive interference is not worth the pains of providing one's self with a trowel and cement. Then why this art of stopping crevices?

Wait. In its apparently peaceful home, in its round shell which seems to give it such perfect security, the grub nevertheless has its troubles. Which of us has not, from the greatest to the smallest? They begin at birth. Though I have only touched the fringe of the matter, I am already aware of three or four sorts of grievous accidents to which the Sacred Beetle's larva is liable. Plants, animals, blind physical forces, all work its ruin by destroying its larder.

Competition is rife around the cake served up by the Sheep. When the mother Scarab arrives to take her share and manufacture her pill, the bit is often at the mercy of fellow-banqueters of whom the smallest are the most to be dreaded. There are especially little Onthophagi, earnest workers crouching under the shelter of the cake. Some prefer to plunge into the richest part and bury themselves ecstatically in its luscious depths. One of these is Schreber's Onthophagus, who is a shiny ebon-black, with four red spots on his wing-cases. Another is the smallest of our Aphodii (*Aphodius pusillus*, Herbst), who confides her eggs, here and there, to the thick part of the cake. In her hurry, the mother Scarab does not examine her harvest very carefully. While some of the Onthophagi are removed, others, buried in the centre of the mass, escape notice. Besides, the Aphodius' eggs are so small that they elude her vigilance. In this way a contaminated lump of paste is taken into the burrow and moulded.

The pears in our gardens suffer from vermin which disfigure them with scars. The Sacred Beetle's pears suffer even worse ravages. The Onthophagus shut in by accident ferrets about and pulls them to pieces. When, filled to repletion, the glutton wishes to make his exit, he pierces them with circular holes large enough to admit a lead-pencil. The evil is worse still with the Aphodius, whose family hatch, develop and undergo their transformation in the very heart of the provisions. My notes contain descriptions of pears perforated in every direction, riddled with a multitude of holes that serve for the escape of the tiny dung-worker, a parasite in spite of himself.

With table-fellows such as these, who bore ventilating-shafts in the provisions, the Sacred Beetle's grub dies if the miners be numerous. Its trowel and mortar cannot cope with so great a task. They can cope with it if the damage be slight and the intruders few. At once stopping up every passage that opens around it, the grub holds its own against the invader; it disgruntles him and drives him away. The pear is saved and preserved from internal desiccation.

Various Cryptogamia have a finger in the pie. They invade the fertile soil of the pill, make it rise in scales, split it with fissures by implanting their pustules. In its shell cracked by this vegetation, the grub would die were it not for the safeguard of its mortar, which puts an end to these desiccating vent-holes.

It puts an end to them in a third case, the most frequent of all. Without the intervention of any ravager, whether animal or plant, the pear pretty often peels of its own accord, swells and tears. Is this due to a reaction in the outer layer, which was too tightly pressed by the mother when modelling? Is it due to an attempt at fermentation? Or is it not rather the result of a contraction similar to that of clay, which splits in drying? All three causes might very well play their part.

But, without saying anything positive on this point, I will draw attention to certain deep fissures which seem to threaten the soft bread with desiccation, inadequately protected as it is by the cracked jar. Have no fear that these spontaneous breaches will do any harm: the larva will soon put them right. In the distribution of gifts, it was not for nothing that the trowel and putty were awarded to the Sacred Beetle's grub.

We will now give a brief description of the larva, without stopping to enumerate the articulations of the palpi and antennæ, which are wearisome details of no immediate interest. It is a fat grub and has a fine, white skin, with pale slate-coloured reflections proceeding from the digestive organs, which are visible when you hold the creature to the light. Bent into a broken arch or hook, it is not unlike the grub of the Cockchafer, but has a much more ungainly figure, for, on its back, at the sudden bend of the hook, the third, fourth and fifth segments of the abdomen swell into an enormous hump, a tumour, a bag so prominent that the skin seems on the point of bursting under the pressure of the contents. This is the animal's most striking feature: the fact that it carries a knapsack.

The head is small, in proportion to the grub's size, is slightly convex, bright-red and studded with a few pale bristles. The legs are fairly long and sturdy, ending in a pointed tarsus. The grub does not use them as a means of progression. When taken from its shell and placed upon the table, it struggles in clumsy contortions without succeeding in shifting its position; and the helpless creature betrays its anxiety by repeated discharges of its mortar.

Let us also mention the terminal trowel, that last segment lopped into a slanting disk and rimmed with a fleshy pad. In the centre of this inclined plane is the open stercoraceous slit, which thus, by a very unusual inversion, occupies the upper surface. A huge hump and a trowel: that gives you the insect in two words.

In his *Histoire naturelle des coléoptères de France,* Mulsant describes the larva of the Sacred Beetle. He tells us with meticulous detail the number and shape of the joints of the palpi and antennæ; he sees the hypopygium4 and its pointed bristles; he sees a multitude of things in the domain of the microscope; and he does not see the monstrous knapsack that takes up almost half the insect, nor does he see the strange configuration of the last segment. There is not a doubt in my mind that the writer of this minute description has made a mistake: the larva of which he speaks is nothing like that of the Sacred Beetle.

We must not finish the history of the grub without saying a few words about its internal structure. Anatomy will show us the works wherein the cement employed in so eccentric a manner is manufactured. The stomach or chylific ventricle is a long, thick cylinder, starting from the creature's neck after a very short œsophagus. It measures about three times the insect's length. In its last quarter, it carries a voluminous lateral pocket distended by the food. This is a subsidiary stomach in which the supplies are stored so as to yield their nutritive principles more thoroughly. The chylific ventricle is much too long to lie straight and twists round in front of its appendix, in the form of a large loop occupying the dorsal surface. It is to contain this loop and the side-pocket that the back swells into a hump. The grub's knapsack is, therefore, a second paunch, an annexe, as it were, of the stomach, which is by itself incapable of holding the voluminous digestive apparatus. Four very fine, very long tubular glands, very much entangled, four Malpighian vessels mark the limits of the chylific ventricle.

Next comes the intestine, which is narrow and cylindrical and rises in front. The intestine is followed by the rectum, which pushes backwards. This last, which is exceptionally large and furnished with stout walls, is wrinkled across, bloated and distended with its contents. There you have the roomy warehouse in which the digestive refuse accumulates; there you have the mighty ejaculator, ever ready to provide cement.

1 Cf. *The Life and Love of the Insect*, by J. Henri Fabre, translated by Alexander Teixeira de Mattos: chap. xi.—*Translator's Note.*

2 Cf. *The Hunting Wasps,* by J. Henri Fabre, translated by Alexander Teixeira de Mattos: chaps, iv. to x.—*Translator's Note.*

3 ·19 inch.—*Translator's Note.*

4 The last ventral segment of the abdomen.—*Translator's Note.*

CHAPTER VII
THE SACRED BEETLE: THE NYMPH; THE RELEASE

The larva increases in bulk as it eats the walls of its house from the inside. Little by little, the belly of the pear is scooped out into a cell whose capacity grows in proportion to the growth of its inhabitant. Ensconced in its hermitage, supplied with board and lodging, the recluse waxes big and fat. What more is wanted? Certain hygienic duties have to be attended to, though it is no easy matter in a cramped little niche nearly all the room in which is occupied by the grub; the mortar incessantly elaborated by an excessively obliging intestine must be shot somewhere when there is no breach that needs repairing.

The larva is certainly not fastidious, but even so the bill of fare must not be too outrageous. The humblest of the humble does not return to what he or his kin have already digested. Matter from which the intestinal alembic has extracted the last available atom yields nothing more, unless we change both chemist and apparatus. What the Sheep, with her fourfold stomach, has left behind as worthless residue is an excellent thing for the grub, which also boasts a mighty paunch; but the larva's own droppings, though no doubt pleasing in their turn to consumers of another class, are loathsome to the grub itself. Then where shall the cumbrous refuse be stored, in a lodging of such niggardly dimensions?

I have described elsewhere the singular industry of the Cotton-bees,1 whose larvæ, in order not to foul their provision of honey, make from their digestive dregs an elegant casket, a masterpiece of inlaid work. With the only material at its disposal in its secluded retreat, with the filth that apparently ought to be an intolerable nuisance, the grub of the Sacred Beetle produces a work less artistic than the Cotton-bee's but much more comfortable. Let us see how it is done.

Attacking its pear at the bottom of the neck, eating steadily downwards and leaving nothing intact in its area of operations except a flimsy wall necessary for its protection, the larva obtains a free space at the back, in which its droppings are deposited without dirtying the provisions. The hatching-chamber is the first to be filled up in this way; then gradually more and more of the segment which has been eaten into follows suit, always in the round part of the pear, which consequently by degrees recovers its original compactness at the top, while the bottom becomes less and less thick. Behind the grub is the ever-increasing mass of used material; in front of it is the layer, smaller day by day, of untouched food.

Complete development is attained in four or five weeks. By that time there is in the belly of the pear an eccentric circular cavity, with walls very thick towards the neck of the pear and very flimsy at the other end, the disparity being occasioned by the method of eating and of progressive filling up. The meal is over. Next comes the furnishing of the cell, which must be padded snugly for the tender body of the nymph, and the strengthening of one of the hemispheres, the one whose walls have been scraped by the last bites to the utmost permissible limit.

For this most important work the larva has wisely reserved a plentiful stock of cement. The trowel therefore begins to be busy. This time, the object is not to repair damage; it is to double and treble the thickness of the wall in the weaker hemisphere and to cover the whole surface with stucco which, after being polished by the movements of the grub's body, will be soft to the touch. As this cement acquires a consistency superior to that of the original materials, the grub is at last contained within a stout casket which defies all efforts to open it with one's fingers and is almost capable of withstanding a blow from a stone.

The apartment is ready. The grub sheds its skin and becomes a nymph. There are very few inhabitants of the insect world that can compare for sober beauty with the delicate creature which, with wing-cases recumbent in front of it like a wide-pleated scarf and fore-legs folded under its head like those of the adult Beetle when counterfeiting death, calls to mind a mummy kept by its linen bandages in the approved hieratic attitude. Semitranslucent and honey-yellow, it looks as though it were carved from a block of amber. Imagine it hardened in this state, mineralized, rendered incorruptible: it would make a splendid topaz gem.

In this marvel of beauty, so severe and dignified in shape and colouring, one point above all captivates me and at last provides me with the solution of a far-reaching problem. Have the fore-legs a tarsus, yes or no? This is the great matter that makes me neglect the jewel for the sake of a structural detail. Let us then return to a subject that used to excite me in my early days, for the answer has come at last, late, it is true, but certain and indisputable. The probabilities which were all that my first investigations could give me turn into certainties established by overwhelming evidence.

By a very strange exception, the full-grown Sacred Beetle and his congeners have no front tarsi: they lack on their fore-limbs the five-jointed finger which is the rule among the highest section of Beetles, the Pentamera.

The remaining legs, on the other hand, follow the general law and possess a very well-shaped tarsus. Does this curious formation of the toothed fore-arms date from birth, or is it accidental?

At first sight, an accident seems not unlikely. The Sacred Beetle is a strenuous miner and a great pedestrian. Always in contact with the rough soil, whether in walking or digging, used moreover for constant leverage when the insect is rolling its pill backwards, the front limbs are exposed much more freely than the others to the danger of spraining and twisting their delicate finger, of putting it out of joint, of losing it entirely, from the first moment when the work begins.

Lest this explanation should appeal to any of my readers, I will hasten to undeceive him. The absence of the front fingers is not the result of an accident. Here before my eyes lies the unanswerable proof. I examine the nymph's legs with the magnifying glass: those in front have not the least vestige of a tarsus; the toothed limb ends bluntly, without any trace of a terminal appendage. In the others, on the contrary, the tarsus is as distinct as can be, notwithstanding the shapeless, lumpy condition due to the swaddling-bands and humours of the nymphal state. It suggests a finger swollen with chilblains.

If the evidence of the nymph were not sufficient, there would still be that of the perfect insect, which, casting its mummy-cloths and moving for the first time in its shell, wields fingerless fore-arms. The point is established for a certainty: the Sacred Beetle is born maimed; his mutilation dates from the beginning.

'Very well,' our popular theorists will reply, 'the Sacred Beetle is mutilated from birth; but his remote ancestors were not. Formed according to the general rule, they were correct in structure down to this tiny digital detail. There were some who, in their rough work as navvies and carters, wore out that fragile, useless member which was always in the way; and, finding themselves all the better equipped for their work by this accidental amputation, they bequeathed it to their successors, to the great benefit of their race. The present insect profits by the improvement obtained by a long array of ancestors and, acting under the stimulus of the struggle for life, gives more and more durability to a favourable condition due to chance.'

O ingenious theorists, so triumphant on paper, so impotent in the face of facts, just listen to me for a moment! If the loss of the front fingers is a fortunate circumstance for the Sacred Beetle, who faithfully transmits the leg of olden time fortuitously maimed, why should it not be so with the other limbs, if they too chanced to lose their terminal appendage, a tiny, feeble filament, which is very nearly useless and which, owing to its fragility, is a cause of awkward encounters with the roughness of the soil?

The Sacred Beetle is not a climber; he is an ordinary pedestrian, supporting himself upon the point of an iron-shod stick, whereby I mean the stout spike or prickle with which the tip of his leg is armed. He has no occasion to hold on by his claws to some hanging branch, as the Cockchafer does. It would therefore, meseems, be entirely to his advantage to rid himself of the four remaining digits, which jut out sideways, give no help in walking, and do not play any part in the making and the carting of the ball. Yes, that would mean progress, for the simple reason that the less hold you give the enemy the better. It remains to be seen if chance ever produces this state of things.

It does and very often. At the end of the fine weather, in October, when the insect has worn itself out in digging, in trundling pills and in modelling pears, the maimed, disabled by their exertions, form the great majority. Both in my cages and out of doors, I see them in all stages of mutilation. Some have lost the finger on their four hind-limbs altogether; others retain a stump, a couple of joints, a single joint; those least damaged have a few members left intact.

Here then is the mutilation on which the philosophers base their theory. And it is no rare accident: every year the cripples outnumber the others when the time comes for retiring to winter-quarters. In their final labours they seem no more embarrassed than those who have been spared by the buffeting of life. On both sides I find the same nimbleness of movement, the same dexterity in kneading the reserve of bread which will enable them to bear the first rigours of winter with equanimity in their underground homes. In scavenger's work, the maimed rival the others.

And these cripples found families: they spend the cold season beneath the soil; they wake up in the spring, return to the surface and take part for a second time, sometimes even for a third, in life's great festival. Their descendants ought to profit by an improvement which has been renewed year by year, ever since Sacred Beetles came into the world, and which has certainly had time to become fixed and to convert itself into a settled habit. But they do nothing of the sort. Every Sacred Beetle that breaks his shell, with not one exception, is endowed with the regulation four tarsi.

Well, my theorists, what do you say to that? For the two front legs you offer a sort of explanation; and the four others give you a categorical denial. Have you not been taking your fancies for facts?

Then what is the cause of the Sacred Beetle's original mutilation? I will frankly confess that I have no idea. Nevertheless those two maimed members are very strange, so strange indeed that they have enticed the masters, the greatest masters, into lamentable errors. Listen, first of all, to Latreille,[2] the prince of descriptive entomologists. In his article on the insects which ancient Egypt painted or carved upon her monuments,[3] he quotes the writings of Horapollo,4 a unique document preserved for us in the papyri for the glorification of the sacred insect:

> 'One would be tempted at first,' he says, 'to set down as fiction what Horapollo says of the number of this Beetle's fingers: according to him, there are thirty. Nevertheless, this computation, judged by the way in which he looks at the tarsus, is quite correct, for this part consists of five joints; and, if we take each of them for a finger, the legs being six in number and each ending in a five-jointed tarsus, the Sacred Beetles evidently had thirty fingers.'

Forgive me, illustrious master: the number of joints is but twenty, because the two fore-legs are without tarsi. You were carried away by the general rule. Losing sight of the singular exception, which you certainly knew, you said thirty, obsessed for a moment by that overwhelmingly positive rule. Yes, you knew the exception, so much so that the figure of the Scarab accompanying your article, a figure drawn from the insect and not from the Egyptian monuments, is irreproachably accurate: it has no tarsi on its front legs. The blunder is pardonable, because the exception is so unusual.

Mulsant,5 in his volume on the French Lamellicorns, quotes Horapollo and his allowance of thirty fingers to the insect according to the number of days which the sun takes to traverse a sign of the Zodiac. He repeats Latreille's explanation. He goes even farther. Here are his own words:

> 'If we count each joint of the tarsi as a finger, we must admit that this insect was examined with great attention.'

Examined with great attention! By whom, pray? By Horapollo? Not a bit of it! By you, my master: yes, indeed yes! And yet the rule, in its very positiveness, is misleading you for a moment; it misleads you again and in a more serious fashion when, in your illustration of the Sacred Beetle, you represent the insect with tarsi on its fore-legs, tarsi similar to those on the other legs. You, painstaking describer though you be, have in your turn been the victim of a momentary aberration. The rule is so general that it has made you lose sight of the singularity of the exception.

What did Horapollo himself see? Apparently what we see in our day. If Latreille's explanation be right, as everything seems to indicate, if the Egyptian author began by counting the first thirty fingers according to the number of joints in the tarsi, it is because he made a mental enumeration on the basis of the general circumstances. He was guilty of a slip which was not so very reprehensible, seeing that, more than a thousand years later, masters like Latreille and Mulsant were guilty of the same slip. If we must blame something, let us blame the exceptional structure of the insect.

'But,' I may be asked, 'why should not Horapollo have seen the exact truth? Perhaps the Sacred Beetle of his day had tarsi which the insect no longer possesses. In that case, it has been transformed by the slow work of time.'

I am waiting for some one to show me a natural Scarab of Horapollo's period before I reply to this objection on the part of the evolutionists. The tombs which so religiously guard the Cat, the Ibis and the Crocodile must also contain the sacred insect. All that I have by me is a few figures showing the Scarab as we find him engraved on the monuments or carved in fine stone as an amulet for the mummies. The ancient artist is remarkably faithful in the execution of the thing as a whole; but his graver and chisel have not troubled about such insignificant details as the tarsi.

Poor as I am in documents of this kind, I doubt whether the work of sculptor or engraver will solve the problem. Even if an image with front tarsi were discovered somewhere or other, the question would be no further advanced. It would always be possible to plead a mistake, an oversight, a leaning towards symmetry. The doubt, so long as it prevails in certain minds, can be removed only by the sight of the ancient insect in the natural state. I will wait for it, though convinced beforehand that the Sacred Beetle of the Pharaohs differed in no way from our own.

We will stay a little longer with the old Egyptian author, though his wild allegorical jargon is usually incomprehensible. He is sometimes strikingly accurate in his ideas. Is this due to a chance coincidence? Or is it the result of serious observation? I should be glad to take the latter view, so perfect is the agreement between his statements and certain biological details of which our own science was ignorant until quite lately. Of the home life of the Sacred Beetle Horapollo knew much more than we do. He tells us this in particular:

> 'The Scarabæus deposits this ball in the earth for the space of twenty-eight days (for in so many days the moon passes through the twelve signs of the Zodiac). By thus remaining under the moon the race of Scarabæi is endowed with life; and upon the twenty-ninth day, after having opened the ball, it casts it into water, for it is aware that upon that day the conjunction of the moon and sun takes place, as well as the generation of the world. From the ball thus opened, the animals, that is, the Scarabæi, issue forth.'6

Let us dismiss the revolution of the moon, the conjunction of the sun and moon, the generation of the world and other astrological absurdities, but remember this, the twenty-eight days of incubation required by the ball underground, the twenty-eight days during which the Scarab is born to life. Let us also remember the indispensable intervention of water to bring the insect out of its burst shell. These are definite facts, falling within the domain of true science. Are they imaginary or real? The question deserves investigation.

The ancients were unacquainted with the wonders of the metamorphosis. To them a larva was a worm born of corruption. The wretched creature had no future to lift it from its abject state: as worm it appeared and as worm it must disappear. It was not a mask whereunder a higher form of life was being elaborated; it was a definite entity, supremely contemptible and doomed soon to return to the putrescence of which it was the offspring.

To the Egyptian author, then, the Scarab's larva was unknown. And, if by chance he had had before his eyes the insect's shell inhabited by a fat, pot-bellied grub, he would never have suspected in the foul and ugly animal the sober beauty of the future Scarab. According to the ideas of the time, ideas that were long maintained, the sacred insect had neither father nor mother: an error excusable among the untutored ancients, for here the two sexes are outwardly indistinguishable. It was born of the ordure that formed its ball; and its birth dated from the appearance of the nymph, that amber jewel displaying, in a perfectly recognizable shape, the features of the adult insect.

In the eyes of antiquity the life of the Sacred Beetle began at the moment when he could be recognized, not before; for otherwise we should have that as yet unsuspected connecting-link, the grub. The twenty-eight days, therefore, during which, as Horapollo tells us, the offspring of the insect quickens, represent the duration of the nymphal phase. This duration has been the object of special attention in my studies. It varies but never to any great extent. From my notes I find thirty-three days to be the longest period and twenty-one the shortest. The average, supplied by some twenty observations, is twenty-eight days. This very number twenty-eight, this number of days contained in four weeks, actually appears oftener than the others. Horapollo spoke truly: the real insect takes life in the space of a lunar month.

The four weeks passed, behold the Sacred Beetle in his final shape: the shape, yes, but not the colouring, which is very strange when the nymph casts its skin. The head, legs and thorax are dark-red, except the denticulations of the forehead and fore-arms, which are smoky-brown. The abdomen is an opaque white; the wing-cases are semitransparent white, very faintly tinged with yellow. This imposing raiment, blending the scarlet of the cardinal's cassock with the white of the celebrant's alb, a raiment that harmonizes with the insect's hieratic character, is but temporary and turns darker by degrees, to make way for a uniform of ebon black. About a month is needed for the horny armour to acquire a firm consistency and a definite hue.

At last the Beetle is fully matured. Awakening within him is the delicious restlessness born of coming freedom. He, hitherto a son of the darkness, foresees the gladness of the light. Great is his longing to burst the shell so that he may emerge from his underground prison and come into the sun; but the difficulty of liberating himself is no small one. Will he or will he not escape from the natal cradle, which has now become a hateful dungeon? It depends.

Generally in August the Sacred Beetle is ripe for release: in August, save for rare exceptions, the most torrid, dry and scorching month of the year. If therefore no shower come from time to time to give some slight relief to the panting earth, then the cell to be burst and the wall to be breached defy the strength and patience of the insect, which is helpless against all that hardness. Owing to prolonged desiccation, the soft original matter has become an insuperable rampart; it has turned into a sort of brick baked in the kiln of summer.

I have, of course, made experiments on the insect in these difficult circumstances. I gather pear-shaped shells containing the adult Beetle, who is on the point of emerging, in view of the lateness of the season. These shells are already dry and very hard; and I lay them in a box where they retain their dryness. Sooner or later I hear the sharp grating of a rasp inside each cell. It is the prisoner working to make himself an outlet by scraping the wall with the rake of his forehead and fore-feet. Two or three days elapse; and the process of deliverance seems to be no further advanced.

I come to the assistance of a pair of them by myself opening a loophole with a knife. My idea is that this first breach will help the egress of the recluse by giving him a place to start upon, an exit that will only need widening. But not at all: these favoured ones make no more progress with their work than the others.

In less than a fortnight silence prevails in all the shells. The prisoners, worn out with vain endeavours, have perished. I break the caskets containing the deceased. A meagre pinch of dust, hardly as much as an average pea in bulk, is all that those powerful implements, rasp, saw, harrow and rake, have succeeded in detaching from the invincible wall.

I take some other shells, of equal hardness, wrap them in a wet rag and put them in a flask. When the moisture has soaked through them, I rid them of their wrapper and keep them in the corked flask. This time events take a very different course. Softened to a nicety by the wet rag, the shells open, burst by the efforts of the prisoner, who props himself boldly on his legs, using his back as a lever; or else, scraped away at one point, they crumble to pieces and reveal a yawning breach. The experiment is a complete success. In every case the release of the Beetles is safely accomplished: a few drops of water have brought them the joys of the sun.

For the second time Horapollo was right. True, it is not the mother, as the ancient writer says, who throws her ball into the water: it is the clouds that provide the liberating douche, it is the rain that brings about the ultimate release. In the natural state things must happen as in my experiments. When the soil is burnt by the August sun, the shells, baked like bricks under their thin covering of earth, are for most of the time hard as stones. It is impossible for the insect to wear away its casket and escape. But let a shower come—that life-giving baptism which the seed of the plant and the family of the Beetle alike await within the cinders of the earth—let a little rain fall; and soon there will be a resurrection in the fields.

The earth becomes soaked. There you have the wet rag of my experiment. At its touch the shell recovers the softness of its early days, the casket becomes yielding; the insect makes play with its legs and pushes with its back; it is free. It is in fact in September, during the first rains that herald autumn, that the Sacred Beetle leaves his native burrow and comes forth to enliven the pastoral sward, even as the former generation enlivened it in the spring. The clouds, hitherto so ungenerous, at last set him free.

When the earth is exceptionally cool, the bursting of the shell and the deliverance of its occupant can occur at an earlier period; but in ground scorched by the pitiless summer sun, as is usually the case in my district, the Beetle, however eager he may be to see the light, must needs wait for the first rain to soften his stubborn shell. A downpour is to him a question of life and death. Horapollo, that echo of the Egyptian magi, saw true when he made water play its part in the birth of the sacred insect.

But let us drop the jargon of antiquity, with its fragments of truth; let us not overlook the first acts of the Scarab on leaving his shell; and let us be present at his prentice steps in open-air life. In August I break the casket in which I hear the helpless captive chafing. I place the insect, the only one of its species, in a cage together with some Gymnopleuri. There is plenty of fresh food provided. This is the moment, said I to myself, when we take refreshment after so long an abstinence. Well, I was wrong: the new recruit shows no interest in the victuals, notwithstanding my invitations, my summons to the tempting heap. What he wants above all is the joys of the light. He scales the metal trelliswork, sets himself in the sun, and there motionless takes his fill of its beams.

What passes through his dull-witted Dung-beetle brain during this first bath of radiant brightness? Probably nothing. His is the unconscious happiness of a flower blossoming in the sun.

At last the insect goes to the victuals. A pellet is made in accordance with all the rules. There is no apprenticeship: at the first attempt, the spherical form is achieved as accurately as after long practice. A burrow is dug in which the bread just kneaded may be eaten in peace. Here again we find the novice thoroughly versed in his art. No length of experience will add anything to his talents.

His digging-tools are his fore-legs and forehead. To shoot the rubbish outside, he uses the barrow, exactly like any of his elders, that is to say, he covers his corselet with a load of earth; then, head downwards, he dives into the dust, afterwards coming forward and depositing his load a few inches from the entrance. With a leisurely step, like that of a navvy with a long job before him, he goes underground again to reload his barrow. This work upon the dining-room takes whole hours to finish.

At length the ball is stored away. The front-door is shut; and the thing is done. Bed and board secured, begone dull care! All is for the best in the best of all possible worlds. Lucky creature! Without ever seeing it practised by your kindred, whom you have not yet met, without ever learning it, you know your trade to perfection; and it will give you an ample share of food and tranquillity, both so hard to achieve in human life.

1 Cf. *Bramble-bees and Others*, by J. Henri Fabre, translated by Alexander Teixeira de Mattos: chap. ix.—*Translator's Note.*

2 Pierre André Latreille (1762–1833), one of the founders of entomological science, a professor at the *Muséum d'histoire naturelle* and member of the *Académie des sciences.—Translator's Note.*

3 Cf. *Mémoires du Muséum d'histoire naturelle*: vol. v., p. 249.—*Author's Note.*

4 Horapollo Nilous, Orus Apollo, or Horos Apollo (*fl. circa 400*), author of the *Hieroglyphica.—Translator's Note.*

5 Etienne Marcel Mulsant (1797–1880), author of the *Histoire naturelle des coléoptères en France* (1839–1874) mentioned on page 94.—*Translator's Note.*

6 *Hieroglyphics*: Book 1., x.; Cory's translation.—*Translator's Note.*

CHAPTER VII
THE BROAD-NECKED SCARAB; THE GYMNOPLEURI

What we have learnt from the Sacred Beetle must not lead us into rash generalizations and make us attribute it in every slightest detail to the other Dung-beetles of the same family. Similarity of structure does not entail parity of instincts. A common basis no doubt exists, resulting from identity of equipment; but many variations of the essential theme are possible and are dictated by inherent aptitudes of which the insect's organization gives us no inkling. In fact, the study of these variations, of these peculiarities, with their hidden reasons, forms the most attractive part of the observer's researches as he explores his corner of the entomological domain. Unsparing of time and patience, sometimes of ingenuity, you have at last learnt what this one does. See now what that one does, his near neighbour structurally. To what extent does number two repeat the habits of number one? Has he ways of his own, tricks of the trade, industrial specialities unknown to the other? It is a highly interesting problem, for the impassable line of demarcation between the two species is much more conspicuous in these psychological differences than in the differences of the wing-case or antenna.

The Scarab clan is represented in my district by the Sacred Beetle (*Scarabæus sacer*, Lin.), the Half-spotted Scarab (*S. semipunctatus*, Fab.) and the Broad-necked Scarab (*S. laticollis*, Lin.). The two former are chilly creatures and hardly stir from the Mediterranean; the third goes pretty far north. The Half-spotted Scarab does not leave the coast; he abounds on the sandy beaches of the Golfe Juan, Cette and Palavas. I have, in my time, admired his prowess at pill-rolling, of which he is as fervent a devotee as his colleague the Sacred Beetle. To-day, though we are old friends, I cannot, to my great regret, give my attention to him: we are too far away from each other. I recommend him to any one wishing to add a chapter to Scarab biography: he also must have—I feel nearly sure of it—peculiarities worth noting.

And so, to complete this study, there remains in my immediate proximity only the Broad-necked Scarab, the smallest of the three. He is very rare around Sérignan, though widely distributed in other parts of the Vaucluse. This scarcity deprives me of opportunities for observing the insect in the open fields; and my only resource is to bring up a few chance specimens in captivity.

Behind the wire-gauze of his prison, the Broad-necked Scarab does not display the Sacred Beetle's athletic prowess nor his bold and hasty temper. In his case we see no scuffles between robber and robbed, no pills manufactured purely for art's sake, rolled for a little while with wild enthusiasm and then consigned to the rubbish-heap without being employed at all. The same blood does not flow in the veins of the two pill-rollers.

Of a quieter disposition and less wasteful of his gleanings, the Beetle with the broad corselet attacks discreetly the heap of manna provided by the Sheep; he picks from the best part some armfuls of material which he makes into a ball; he attends to his business without troubling the others or being troubled by them. For the rest, his methods are the same as those of the Sacred Beetle. The sphere, which is always an easier object to convey, is fashioned on the spot before being set in motion. With his wide fore-legs the Beetle pats and kneads and moulds it, making it smooth and level by adding an armful here and there. The perfect roundness of the ball is achieved before it leaves the place.

When the requisite size has been obtained, the pill-roller makes his way with his booty to the spot where the burrow is to be dug. The journey is effected exactly as it would be by the Sacred Beetle. Head downwards, hind-legs lifted against the rolling mechanism, the insect pushes backwards. So far there is nothing new, save for a certain slowness in the performance. But wait a little while: soon a striking difference in habits will separate the two insects.

As each pill is carted away, I seize it, together with its owner, and place both on the surface of a layer of fresh, close-packed sand in a flower-pot. A sheet of glass serves as a lid, keeps the sand nice and cool, prevents escape and admits the light. By interning each Beetle separately, I am saved from the mistakes which might arise if I put them in the common cage, where a number of my boarders are at work; and I shall not risk ascribing to several what may be the performance of one alone. By this solitary confinement, each individual Beetle's work can be studied more easily.

The interned mother makes hardly any protest against her servitude. Soon she is digging the sand and disappears in it with her pill. Let us give her time to establish her quarters and to get on with her domestic labours.

Three or four weeks go by. The Beetle has not reappeared upon the surface, a proof of her patient absorption in her maternal duties. At last I remove the contents of the pot, very carefully, layer by layer, until I uncover a spacious burrow. The rubbish from this cavity was heaped up on the surface, forming a little mound. This is the secret chamber, the gynæceum in which the mother now and for a long time to come keeps watch over her budding family.

The original pill has disappeared. In its stead are two little pears, elegantly shaped and wonderfully finished: two, not one, as I naturally expected from the information already in my possession. They strike me as being even more delicately and gracefully rounded than the Sacred Beetle's. Perhaps their tiny dimensions cause my preference: *maxime miranda in minimis*. They measure 33 millimetres in length and 24 millimetres across their greatest width.1 Let us drop figures and admit that the dumpy modeller, with her slow and awkward ways, is the artistic rival or even the superior of her famous kinswoman. I expected to see some clumsy apprentice; I find a consummate artificer. We must not judge people by appearances; it is a wise maxim, even when applied to insects.

If we examine the pot somewhat earlier, it will tell us how the pear is made. I find sometimes a perfectly round ball and a pear without any traces of the original pill; sometimes a ball only, with a nearly hemispherical remnant of the pill, a lump from which the materials subjected to modelling have been detached in one piece. The method of work can be deduced from these facts.

The pill which the Scarab fashions on the surface of the soil by taking armfuls from the heap encountered is but a temporary piece of work, which is given a round form with the sole object of facilitating its transport. He gives his attention to it, no doubt, but is not unduly anxious about it; all that he wants is that the journey should be effected without any crumbling of his treasure or impediment in the rolling. The surface of the sphere, therefore, is not thoroughly treated; it is not compressed into a rind or made scrupulously even.

Underground, when it is a question of getting the egg's casket ready, the casket that is to be both larder and cradle, it becomes another matter. An incision is made all round the pill, dividing it into two almost equal portions, and one half is subjected to manipulation, while the other lies just against it, destined to receive the same treatment later. The hemisphere worked upon is rounded into a ball, which will be the belly of the prospective pear. This time, the modelling is performed with the nicest care: the future of the larva, which also is exposed to the dangers of overdry bread, is at stake. The surface of the ball is therefore patted at one spot after the other, conscientiously hardened by compression and levelled along a regular curve. The spherule thus obtained possesses geometrical precision, or very nearly so. Let us not forget that this difficult work is accomplished without rolling, as the clean condition of the surface shows.

The rest of the business may be guessed from the proceedings of the Sacred Beetle. The sphere is hollowed into a crater and becomes a sort of bulging, shallow pot. The lips are drawn out into a pocket which receives the egg. The pocket is closed, polished outside and joined neatly to the sphere. The pear is finished. The other half of the pill is now similarly treated.

The notable feature of this work is the elegant regularity of the forms obtained without any rolling. Chance enables me to add another and a most striking proof to the many that I have given of this modelling done on the spot. Once and once only I managed to get from the Broad-necked Scarab two pears closely soldered together by their bellies and lying in opposite directions. The first one constructed can teach us nothing new, but the second tells us this: when, for a reason that is not apparent, for lack of room perhaps, the insect left this second pear touching the other and soldered it to its neighbour while working at it, obviously, with this appendage, any rolling or any moving became impracticable. Nevertheless, the pretty shape was secured to perfection.

From the point of view of instinct, the distinguishing features which make of the two pear-modellers two entirely different species are absolutely clear from these details and much more conclusive than the peculiarities in the corselet and wing-case. The Sacred Beetle's burrow never contains more than one pear. The Broad-necked Scarab's contains two. I even suspect that there are sometimes three, when the haul is a large one: we shall learn more on this subject from the Copres. The first, when she gets her pill underground, uses it just as she obtained it in the workyard and does not subdivide it at all. The second breaks up hers, though it is a little smaller, into two equal parts and fashions each half into a pear. The single ball gives place to two and sometimes even perhaps to three. If the two Dung-beetles have a common origin, I should like to know how this radical difference in their domestic economy declared itself.

The story of the Gymnopleuri is the same as that of the Scarabs, on a more modest scale. To pass it over in silence, for fear of too much sameness, would be to deprive ourselves of evidence calculated to confirm certain theories whose truth is established by the recurrence of similar facts. Let us set it forth, in an abridged form.

The Gymnopleurus family owes its name to a lateral notch in the wing-cases, which leaves a part of the sides bare. It is represented in France by two species. One, with smooth wing-cases (*G. pilularius*, Fab.), is fairly common everywhere; the other (*G. flagellatus*, Fab.), stippled on the top with little holes, as though the insect had been pitted with small-pox, is rarer and prefers the south. Both species abound in the pebbly plains of my neighbourhood, where the Sheep pass amid the lavender and thyme. Their shape is not unlike that of the Sacred Beetle; but they are much smaller. For the rest, they have the same habits, the same fields of operation, the same nesting-period: May and June, down to July.

Applying themselves to similar labours, Gymnopleuri and Scarabs are brought into each other's society rather by the force of things than by the love of company. I not infrequently see them settling next door to each other; I even oftener find them seated at the same heap. In bright sunshine the banqueters are sometimes very numerous. The Gymnopleuri predominate largely.

One would be inclined to think that these insects, endowed with powers of nimble and sustained flight, explore the country in swarms and that, when they find rich plunder, they all swoop down upon it at once. Though the sight of so large a crowd might seem to mean something of the kind, I am very sceptical about these expeditions in large squadrons. I am more ready to believe that the Gymnopleuri have come, from everywhere in the neighbourhood, one by one, guided by keenness of scent. What I see is a gathering of individuals who have hastened from every point of the compass, and not the halt of a swarm engaged on a common search. No matter: the teeming colony is at times so numerous that it would be possible to pick up the Gymnopleuri by handfuls.

But they hardly give one time. When the peril is realized, which soon happens, most of them fly off with all speed; the others crouch low and hide themselves under the heap. In a moment the tumult of activity is succeeded by absolute stillness. The Sacred Beetle is not subject to these sudden attacks of panic, which empty the busiest yard in the twinkling of an eye. When surprised at his task and examined at close quarters, however importunately, he impassively continues his work. He knows no fear. Here we see a thorough difference in temperament between insects which are identical in structure and which follow the same trade.

The difference is equally marked in another respect: the Sacred Beetle is a fervent pill-roller. When the ball is made, his supreme felicity, his *summa voluptas,* is to cart it backwards for hours at a time, to juggle with it, so to speak, under a blazing sun. His epithet *pilularius* notwithstanding, the Gymnopleurus does not show so much enthusiasm over a round pellet. Unless he means to feed upon it quietly in a burrow or to use it as a ration for his larva, he never kneads a ball only to roll it about ecstatically and then abandon it when this violent exercise has given him his fill of pleasure.

Both in his wild state and in captivity, the Gymnopleurus makes his meal on the spot where he finds his food; it is hardly his habit to make a round loaf in order to consume it afterwards in some underground retreat. The pill to which the insect owes its name is rolled, so far as I have seen, only in the interests of its family.

The mother takes from the heap the amount of material required for rearing a larva and kneads it into a ball at the spot where it is gathered. Then, going backwards, with her head down, like the Scarabs, she rolls it and finally stores it in a burrow, in order to give it the necessary treatment for the egg to thrive.

Of course the rolling ball never contains the egg. The laying takes place not on the public highway but in the privacy of the subsoil. A burrow is dug, two or three inches deep at most. It is spacious in proportion to its contents, proving that the Sacred Beetle's studio-work is repeated by the Gymnopleurus. I am speaking of that modelling in which the artist must have full liberty of movement. When the egg is laid, the cell remains empty; only the passage is filled up, as witness the little mound outside, the surplus of the unreplaced refuse.

A minute's digging with my pocket-trowel and the humble cabin is laid bare. The mother is often present, occupied in some trifling household duties before quitting the cell for good. In the middle of the room lies her work, the cradle of the germ and the ration of the coming larva. Its shape and size are those of a Sparrow's egg; and I am here speaking of both Gymnopleuri, whose habits and labours are so much alike that I need not distinguish between them. Unless we found the mother beside it, we should be unable to tell whether the ovoid which we have dug up is the work of the smooth or of the pock-marked insect. At most, a slight advantage in size might point to the former; and even so this characteristic is far from trustworthy.

The egg-shape, with its two unequal ends, one large and round, the other more pointed, shaped like an elliptical nipple, or even drawn out into the neck of a pear, confirms the conclusions with which we are already acquainted. An outline of this kind is not obtained by rolling, which is only reconcilable with a sphere. To get it, the mother must knead her lump of stuff. This may be already more or less round, as the result of the work done in the yard whence it came and of the subsequent carting, or it may still be shapeless, if the heap was near enough to allow of immediate storing. In short, once at home, she acts like the Sacred Beetle, and does modelling-work.

The material lends itself well to this. Taken from the most plastic stuff supplied by the Sheep, it is shaped as easily as clay. In this way the graceful, firm, polished ovoid is obtained, a work of art like the pear and as exquisite in its soft curve as a bird's egg.

Where, inside it, is the insect's germ? If we argued rightly when discussing the Sacred Beetle, if really the questions of ventilation and warmth demand that the egg be as near as possible to the surrounding atmosphere, while remaining protected by a rampart, it is evident that the egg must be installed at the small end of the ovoid, behind a thin defensive wall.

And this in fact is where it lies, lodged in a tiny hatching-chamber and wrapped on every side in a blanket of air, which is easily renewed through a slender partition and a matted plug. This position did not surprise me; from what the Sacred Beetle had already taught me I expected it. The point of my knife, this time no novice, went straight to the ovoid's pointed teat and scratched. The egg appeared, magnificently confirming the argument which had at first been merely suspected, then dimly seen and finally changed into certainty by the recurrence of the fundamental facts under varying conditions.

Scarabs and Gymnopleuri are modellers who were not educated in the same school; they differ in the outline of their masterpiece. With the same materials, the first manufacture pears, the second for the most part ovoids; and yet, despite this divergence, they both conform to the essential conditions demanded by the egg and by the grub. The grub wants provisions that are not liable to become prematurely dry. This condition is fulfilled, so far as may be, by giving the mass a round shape, which evaporates less quickly because of its smaller surface. The egg requires unrestricted air and the heat of the sun's rays, conditions which are fulfilled in the one case by the pear with its neck and in the other by the ovoid with its pointed end.

Laid in June, the egg of either species of Gymnopleuri hatches in less than a week. The average is five or six days. Any one who has seen the larva of the Sacred Beetle knows, so far as essentials go, the larva of the two small pill-rollers. In each case it is a big-bellied grub, curved into a hook and carrying a hump or knapsack which contains a portion of the mighty digestive apparatus. The body is cut off slantwise at the back and forms a stercoral trowel, denoting habits similar to those of the Sacred Beetle's larva.

We see repeated, in fact, the peculiarities described in the story of the big pill-roller. In the larval state, the Gymnopleuri also are great excreters, ever ready with mortar to make good the imperilled dwelling. They instantly repair the breaches which I make, either to observe them in the privacy of their home or to provoke their plastering-industry. They fill up the chinks with putty, solder the parts that become disjointed, mend the broken cell. When the nymphosis approaches, the mortar that remains is expended in a layer of stucco, which reinforces and polishes the inner walls.

The same dangers give rise to the same defensive methods. Like the Sacred Beetles', the shell of the Gymnopleuri is liable to crack. The free admission of air to the interior would have disastrous consequences, by drying the food, which must keep soft until the grub has attained its full growth. An intestine which is never empty and which displays unparalleled docility gets the threatened grub out of its trouble. There is no need to enlarge upon this point; the Sacred Beetle has told us all about it.

The insects reared in captivity tell me that, in the Gymnopleuri, the larva lasts seventeen to twenty-five days and the nymph fifteen to twenty. These figures are bound to vary, but within narrow limits. I shall therefore fix each period at approximately three weeks.

Nothing remarkable happens during the nymphal stage. The only thing to be noted is the curious costume worn by the perfect insect on its first appearance. It is the costume which the Sacred Beetle showed us: head, corselet, legs and chest a rusty red; wing-cases and abdomen white. We may add that, being powerless to burst his shell, which has been turned into a strong-box by the heat of August, the prisoner, in order to release himself, waits until the first September rains come to his help and soften the wall.

Instinct, which under normal conditions amazes us with its unerring prescience, astonishes us no less with its dense ignorance when unaccustomed conditions supervene. Each insect has its trade, in which it excels, its series of actions logically arranged. Here it is really a master. Its foresight, though unwitting, here surpasses our deliberate science; its unconscious inspiration is here the superior of our conscious reason. But divert it from its natural course; and forthwith darkness succeeds the splendours of light. Nothing will rekindle the extinguished rays, not even the greatest stimulus that exists, the stimulus of maternity.

I have given many instances of this strange antithesis,2 which is the death-blow to certain theories; I find another and an exceedingly striking one in the Dung-beetles whose story I have now nearly finished telling. We are surprised at this clear vision of the future possessed by our manufacturers of spheres, pears and ovoids; but we are no less surprised by something totally different, namely, the mother's profound indifference to the nursery which but now was the object of her tenderest cares.

My remarks apply equally to the Sacred Beetle and the two Gymnopleuri, all of whom display the same admirable zeal when the grub's comfort has to be assured, and later, with no less unanimity, the same indifference. I surprise the mother in her burrow before she has laid her eggs, or, if the laying be over, before she has added those meticulous after-touches dictated by her exaggerated conscientiousness. I install her in a pot packed full of earth, placing her on the surface of the artificial soil, together with her work, in its more or less advanced state. In this place of banishment, provided that it be quiet, there is not much hesitation. The mother, who until now has held her precious materials tight-clutched, decides to dig a burrow. As the work of excavation progresses, she drags her pellet down with her, for it is a sacred thing with which she must not part at any time, even amid the difficulties of her digging. Soon the cell in which the pear or the ovoid is to be made is in existence at the bottom of the pot.

I now intervene and turn the pot upside down. Everything is topsy-turvy; the entrance-gallery and the terminal hall disappear. I extract the mother and the pellet from the ruins. Once more the pot is filled with earth; and the same test begins all over again. A few hours are enough to restore the courage shaken by all this upheaval. For the second time, the mother buries herself with the heap of provisions destined for the grub. For the second time also, when the establishment is finished, the overturning of the pot unsettles everything. The experiment is renewed. Persisting in its maternal solicitude, if necessary until its strength gives way, the insect again buries itself, together with its sphere.

Four times over, in two days, I have thus seen the mother Beetle bear up under the devastation which I have wrought and start afresh, with touching patience, on the ruined dwelling. I did not think fit to pursue the test. You feel some scruples in submitting maternal affection to such tribulations as these. However, it seems probable that, sooner or later, the exhausted and bewildered insect would have refused to go on digging.

My experiments of this kind are numerous; and they all prove that, when taken from her burrow with her work unfinished, the mother shows indefatigable perseverance in burying and depositing in a place of safety the cradle which has begun to take shape though as yet untenanted. For the sake of a pellet of stuff which the presence of the egg has not yet turned into a sacred thing, she displays exaggerated prudence and caution, as well as amazing foresight. No tricks of the experimenter, no all-upsetting accidents, nothing, unless her strength be worn out, can divert her from her object. She is filled with a sort of indomitable obsession. The future of her race requires that the lump of stuff should descend into the earth; and descend it will, whatever happens.

Now for the other side of the medal. The egg is laid; everything is in order underground. The mother comes out. I take hold of her as she does so; I dig up the pear or ovoid; I place the work and the worker side by side on the surface of the soil, in the conditions that prevailed just now. This assuredly is the right moment for burying the pill. It contains the egg, a delicate thing which a touch of the sun will wither in its thin wrapper. Expose it for fifteen minutes to the heat of the sun's rays; and all will be lost. What will the mother do in this grave emergency?

She does nothing at all. She does not even seem to perceive the presence of the object which was so precious to her yesterday, when the egg was not yet laid. Zealous to excess before the laying is over, she is indifferent afterwards. The finished work no longer concerns her. Imagine a pebble in the place of the ovoid or pear: the mother would treat it no better and no worse. One sole preoccupation urges her: to get away. I can see that by the manner in which she paces the enclosure that keeps her prisoner.

That is instinct's way: it buries perseveringly the lifeless lump and leaves the quickened lump to perish on the surface. The work to be done is everything; the work done no longer counts. Instinct sees the future and knows nothing of the past.

1 1·28 × ·93 inch.—*Translator's Note.*

2 Cf. *inter alia* the author's *Some Reflections upon Insect Psychology*, in *The Mason-Bees*, by J. Henri Fabre, translated by Alexander Teixeira de Mattos: chap. vii.—*Translator's Note.*

CHAPTER IX
THE SPANISH COPRIS: THE LAYING OF THE EGGS

If we show instinct doing for the egg what would be done on the advice of reason matured by study and experience, we achieve a result of no small philosophic importance; and an austere scientific conscience begins to trouble me with scruples. Not that I wish to give science a forbidding aspect: I am convinced that one can say the wisest things without employing a barbarous vocabulary. Clearness is the supreme courtesy of the wielder of the pen. I do my best to observe it. No, the scruple that stops me is of another kind.

I begin to wonder if I am not in this case the victim of an illusion. I say to myself:

'Gymnopleuri and Sacred Beetles, when in the open air, are manufacturers of balls or pills. That is their trade, learnt we know not how, prescribed perhaps by their structure, in particular by their long legs, some of which are slightly curved. When they are making preparations for the egg, is it so wonderful that they continue underground their own ball-making speciality?'

If we leave out of the question the neck of the pear and the projecting tip of the ovoid, details much more difficult to explain, there remains the most important part so far as bulk is concerned, the globular part, a repetition of the thing which the insect makes outside the burrow; there remains the pellet with which the Sacred Beetle plays in the sunshine, sometimes without making any other use of it, the ball which the Gymnopleurus rolls peacefully over the turf.

Then what is the object here of the globular form, the best preventative of desiccation during the heat of summer? This property of the sphere and of its near neighbour, the ovoid, is an accepted physical fact; but it is only by accident that these shapes are the right ones to overcome that difficulty. A creature built for rolling balls across the fields goes on making balls underground. If the grub fare all the better for finding tender foodstuffs under its mandibles to the very end, that is a capital thing for the grub, but it is no reason why we should extol the instinct of the mother.

So I argued, saying to myself that, before I was convinced, I should need to be shown a Dung-beetle who was utterly unfamiliar with the pill-making business in everyday life and who yet, when laying-time was at hand, made an abrupt change in her habits and shaped her provisions into a ball. My Dung-beetle would have to be a good fat one too. Is there any such in my neighbourhood? Yes, there is; and she is one of the handsomest and largest, next to the Sacred Beetle. I speak of the Spanish Copris (*C. hispanus*, Lin.), who is so remarkable on account of the sharp slope of her corselet and the disproportionate size of the horn surmounting her head.

Round and squat, the Spanish Copris with her ponderous gait is certainly a stranger to gymnastics such as are performed by the Sacred Beetle or the Gymnopleurus. Her legs, which are of insignificant length and folded under her belly at the slightest alarm, bear no comparison with the stilts of the pill-rollers. Their stunted form and lack of flexibility are enough in themselves to tell us that their owner would not care to roam about hampered by a rolling ball.

The Copris is indeed of a sedentary habit. Once he has found his provisions, at night or in the evening twilight, he digs a burrow under the heap. It is a rough cavern, large enough to hold an apple. Here is introduced, bit by bit, the stuff that is just over his head or at any rate lying on the threshold of the cavern; here is engulfed, in no definite shape, an enormous supply of victuals, bearing eloquent witness to the insect's gluttony. As long as the hoard lasts, the Copris, engrossed in the pleasures of the table, does not return to the surface. The home is not abandoned until the larder is emptied, when the insect recommences its nocturnal quest, finds a new treasure and scoops out another temporary dwelling.

As his trade is merely that of a gatherer of manure, shovelling in the stuff without any preliminary manipulation, the Copris is evidently quite ignorant, for the time being, of the art of kneading and modelling a globular loaf. Besides, his short, clumsy legs seem utterly irreconcilable with any such art.

In May, or June at latest, comes laying-time. The insect, so ready to fill its own belly with the most sordid materials, becomes particular where the portion of its family is concerned. Like the Sacred Beetle, like the Gymnopleurus, it now wants the soft produce of the Sheep, deposited in a single slab. Even when abundant, the cake is buried on the spot in its entirety. Not a trace of it remains outside. Economy demands that it be collected to the very last crumb.

You see: no travelling, no carting, no preparations. The cake is carried down to the cellar by armfuls, at the very spot where it lies. The insect repeats, with an eye to its grubs, what it did when working for itself. As for the burrow, whose presence is indicated by a good-sized mound, it is a roomy cavern excavated to a depth of some eight inches. I observe that it is more spacious and better built than the temporary abodes occupied by the Copris at times of revelry.

But let us turn from the insect in its wild state to the insect in captivity. In the former case the evidence furnished by chance encounters would be incomplete, fragmentary and of dubious relevancy; and we shall do better to watch the Copris in my insect-house, especially as she lends herself admirably to this sort of observation. Let us observe the storing first.

In the soft evening light I see her appear on the threshold of her burrow. She has come up from the depths, she is going to gather in her harvest. She has not far to go: the provisions are there, outside the door, a generous supply which I am careful to replenish. Cautiously, ready to retreat at the least alarm, she makes her way to them with a slow and measured step. Her shield does the rummaging and dissecting, her fore-legs are busy extracting. An armful, quite a modest one, is pulled away, crumbling to pieces. The Copris drags it backwards and disappears underground. In less than two minutes, she is back again. With feathery antennæ outspread, she warily scans the neighbourhood before crossing the threshold of her dwelling.

A distance of two or three inches separates her from the heap of provisions. It is a serious matter for her to venture so far. She would have liked the victuals to be exactly overhead, forming a roof to her house. That would have saved her from having to make these expeditions, which are a source of anxiety. I have decided otherwise. To facilitate observation, I have placed the supplies just on one side. By degrees the nervous creature is reassured; it becomes accustomed to the open air and to my presence, which, of course, I make as unobtrusive as possible. Armful after armful goes down into the cellar. They are always shapeless bits, shreds such as one might pick off with a small pair of pincers.

Having learnt what I want to know about the insect's method of warehousing its provisions, I leave it to its work, which continues for the best part of the night. On the following days, nothing happens; the Copris goes out no more. Enough treasure has been laid up in a single night. Let us wait a while and leave her time to stow away her stuff as she pleases.

Before the week is out, I dig up the soil in my insect-house and bring to light the burrow whose victualling I have been watching. As in the fields, it is a spacious hall with an irregular, elliptic roof and an almost level floor. In a corner is a round hole, similar to the orifice in the neck of a bottle. This is the goods-entrance, opening on a slanting gallery that runs up to the surface of the soil. The walls of this house, which was hollowed out of fresh earth, have been carefully compressed and are strong enough to resist any seismic disturbances caused by my excavations. It is easy to see that the insect, toiling for the future, has put forth all its skill, all its digging-powers, in order to produce lasting work. The banqueting-tent may be a hole hurriedly scooped out, with irregular and none too stable walls, but the permanent dwelling is of larger dimensions and much more carefully built.

I suspect that both sexes have a share in this architectural masterpiece; at least, I often come upon the pair in the burrows destined for the laying of the eggs. The roomy and luxurious apartment was no doubt once the wedding-hall; the marriage was consummated under the mighty dome in the building of which the lover had cooperated: a gallant way of declaring his passion. I also suspect him of lending his partner a hand with the collecting and storing of the provisions. From what I have gathered, he too, strong as he is, shares in this finicking work, collects his armfuls and descends into the crypt. It is a quicker job when there are two to help. But, once the home is well stocked, he retires discreetly, makes his way back to the surface and goes and settles down elsewhere, leaving the mother to her delicate task. His part in the family-mansion is ended.

Now what do we find in this mansion, to which we have seen so many tiny loads of provisions lowered? A mass of small pieces, heaped together anyhow? Not a bit of it. I always find a simple lump, a huge loaf which fills the dwelling except for a narrow passage all round, just wide enough to give the mother room to move.

This sumptuous portion, a regular Twelfth-Night cake, has no fixed shape. I come across some that are ovoid, suggesting a Turkey's egg in form and size; I find some that are a flattened ellipsoid, similar to the common onion; I discover some that are almost round, reminding me of a Dutch cheese; I see some that are circular with a slight swelling on the upper surface, like the loaves of the Provençal peasant or, better still, the egg-cake, the *fougasso à l'iôu* with which he celebrates Easter. In every case the surface is smooth and nicely curved.

There is no mistaking what has happened: the mother has collected and kneaded into one lump the numerous fragments brought down one after the other; out of all those particles she has made a homogeneous thing, by mashing them, working them together and treading on them. Time after time I come across the baker on top of the colossal loaf which makes the Sacred Beetle's pill look so insignificant; she strolls about on the convex surface, which sometimes measures as much as four inches across; she pats the mass, makes it firm and level. I just catch sight of the curious scene, for, the moment she is perceived, the pastry-cook slips down the curved slope and hides away under her cake.

For a further knowledge of the work, for a study of its innermost detail, we shall have to resort to artifice. There is scarcely any difficulty about it. Either my long practice with the Sacred Beetle has made me more skilful in my methods of research, or else the Copris is less reserved and bears the rigours of captivity more philosophically: at any rate, I succeed, without the slightest trouble, in following all the phases of the nest-making to my heart's content.

I employ two methods, each of them adapted for enlightening me on some special points. Whenever the vivarium supplies me with a few large cakes, I take these out of the burrows, together with the mother Copris, and place them in my study. The receptacles are of two sorts, according to whether I want light or darkness. In the former case, I use glass jars with a diameter more or less the same as that of the burrows, say four to five inches. At the bottom of each is a thin layer of fresh sand, quite insufficient to allow the Copris to bury herself in it, but still serving the purpose of sparing the insect the slippery foothold of the actual glass and giving it the illusion of a soil similar to that of which I have just deprived it. With this layer the jar becomes a suitable cage for the mother and her loaf.

I need hardly say that the startled insect would not undertake anything while light prevailed, no matter how dim and tempered. It must have complete darkness, which I produce by means of a cardboard sheath enclosing the jar. By carefully raising this sheath a little, I can surprise the captive at her work whenever I feel inclined, the light in my study being a shaded one, and even watch operations for a time. The reader will notice that this arrangement is much less complex than that which I used when I wished to see the Sacred Beetle engaged in modelling her pear, the simpler method being made possible by the different temperament of the Copris, who is more easy-going than her kinswoman. A dozen of these eclipsed appliances are thus arranged on my large laboratory-table. Any one seeing them standing in a row would take them for a collection of groceries in whity-brown paper bags.

For my dark apparatus I use flower-pots filled with fresh, well-packed sand. The mother and her cake occupy the lower part, which is adapted as a niche by means of a cardboard screen forming a ceiling and supporting the sand above. Or else I simply put the mother on the surface of the sand with a supply of provisions. She digs herself a burrow, does her warehousing, makes herself a home; and things follow the usual course. In all cases I rely upon a sheet of glass, which does duty as a lid, to keep my prisoners safe. These different devices will, I trust, give me information on a delicate point of which I will say more later.

What do the glass jars covered with an opaque sheath teach us? A good many things, all of them interesting, and this to begin with: the big loaf does not owe its curve—which is always regular, no matter how much the actual shape may vary—to any rolling process. Our inspection of the natural burrow has already told us that so large a mass could not have been rolled into a cavity of which it fills almost the whole space. Besides, the strength of the insect would be unequal to moving so great a load.

From time to time I go to the jar for information and on every occasion the same evidence is forthcoming. I see the mother, hoisted on top of the lump, feeling here, feeling there, bestowing little taps, smoothing away the projecting points, perfecting the thing; never do I catch her looking as though she wanted to turn the block. It is clear as daylight: rolling has nothing whatever to do with the matter.

The dough-maker's assiduity, her patient care make me suspect an industrial detail whereof I was far from dreaming. Why so many after-touches to the mass, why so long a wait before making use of it? It is, in fact, a week or more before the insect, still busy with its pressing and polishing, makes up its mind to do something with its hoard.

When the baker has kneaded his dough to the requisite extent, he collects it into a single lump in a corner of the kneading-trough. The leaven will work better in the depths of the voluminous mass. The Copris knows this bakehouse secret. She heaps together all that she has collected in her foraging; she carefully kneads the whole into a provisional loaf and allows it time to improve by virtue of an internal process that gives flavour to the paste and makes it of the right consistency for subsequent manipulations. As long as this chemical process remains unfinished, both the baker and the Copris wait. In the case of the insect, it goes on for some time, a week at least.

At last it is ready. The baker's man divides his lump into smaller lumps, each of which will become a loaf. The Copris does the same thing. By means of a circular cut made with the sharp edge of her forehead and the saw of her fore-legs, she detaches from the mass a piece of the prescribed size. With this stroke there is no hesitation, no after-touches adding a bit here and taking off a bit there. Straight away and with one sharp, decisive cut, she obtains the proper-sized lump.

It now becomes a question of shaping it. Clasping it as best she can in her short arms, so little adapted, one would think, to work of this kind, the Copris rounds her lump of dough by means of pressure and of pressure only. Gravely she moves about on the still shapeless pill, climbs up, climbs down, turns to right and left, above and below; here she methodically applies a little more pressure, there a little less, touching and retouching with unvarying patience, and finally, after twenty-four hours of it, the piece that was all corners has become a perfect sphere, the size of a plum. There, in her crowded studio, with scarcely room to move, the podgy artist has completed her work without once shaking it on its base; by dint of time and patience she has obtained the geometrical sphere which her clumsy tools and her confined space seemed bound to deny her.

For a long time the insect continues to touch up its globe, polishing it affectionately, passing its foot gently to and fro until the least protuberance has disappeared. These meticulous finishing touches seem endless. Towards the end of the second day, however, the sphere is pronounced satisfactory. The mother climbs to the dome of her edifice and there, still by simple pressure, hollows out a shallow crater. In this basin the egg is laid.

Then, with extreme caution, with a delicacy that is most surprising with such rough tools, the lips of the crater are brought together so as to form a vaulted roof over the egg. The mother turns slowly, does a little raking, draws the stuff upwards and finishes the closing-process. This is the most ticklish work of all. A little too much pressure, a miscalculated thrust might easily jeopardize the life of the germ under its thin ceiling.

Every now and then the mother suspends operations. Motionless, with lowered forehead, she seems to be sounding the cavity beneath, to be listening to what is happening inside. All's well, it seems; and once again she resumes her patient toil: the careful, delicate scraping of the sides towards the summit, which begins to taper a little and lengthen out. In this way an ovoid with the small end uppermost takes the place of the original sphere. Under the more or less projecting nipple is the hatching-chamber with the egg. Twenty-four hours more are spent in this minute work. Total: four times round the clock and sometimes longer to construct the sphere, scoop out a basin, lay the egg and shut it in by transforming the sphere into an ovoid.

The insect goes back to the cut loaf and helps itself to a second slice, which, by the same manipulations as before, becomes an ovoid tenanted by an egg. The surplus suffices for a third ovoid, sometimes even for a fourth. I have never seen this number exceeded when the mother had at her disposal only the materials which she had accumulated in the burrow.

The laying is over. Here is the mother in her retreat, which is almost filled by the three or four cradles standing one against the other, pointed end upwards. What will she do now? Go away, no doubt, to recruit her strength a little in the open air after her prolonged fast. He who thinks so is mistaken. She stays. And yet she has eaten nothing since she came underground, taking good care not to touch the loaf, which, divided into equal portions, will provide the sustenance of the family. The Copris is touchingly scrupulous where the children's inheritance is concerned: she is a devoted mother, who braves hunger rather than let her offspring suffer privation.

She braves it for a second reason: to mount guard around the cradles. From the end of June onwards the burrows are difficult to find, because the mounds disappear through the action of storm or wind or the feet of the passers-by. The few which I succeed in discovering always contain the mother dozing beside a group of pills, in each of which a grub, now nearing its complete development, feasts on the fat of the land.

My dark appliances, flower-pots filled with fresh sand, confirm what the fields have taught me. Buried with provisions in the first fortnight in May, the mothers do not reappear on the surface, under the glass lid. They keep hidden in the burrow after laying their eggs; they spend the sultry dog-days with their ovoids, watching them, no doubt, as the glass-jars, with their freedom from subterranean obscurity, tell us.

They come up again at the time of the first autumnal rains in September. But by then the new generation has attained its perfect form. The mother, therefore, enjoys in her underground home that rare privilege for an insect, the joy of knowing her family; she hears her children scratching at the shell to obtain their liberty; she is present at the bursting of the casket which she has fashioned so conscientiously; maybe she helps the exhausted weaklings when the ground has not been cool enough to soften the walls. Mother and progeny leave the underworld together; and together they arrive at the autumn banquets, when the sun is mild and the ovine manna abounds along the paths.

The flower-pots teach us something else. I place on the surface a few separate couples taken from their burrows at the outset of the building-operations. They are given a generous supply of provisions. Each couple buries itself, settles down and starts hoarding; then, after ten days or so, the male reappears on the surface, under the sheet of glass. The other does not stir an inch. The eggs are laid, the food-balls are shaped, patiently rounded and grouped at the bottom of the pot. And all the time, so that he may not disturb the mother in her work, the father remains exiled from the gynæceum. He has climbed to the surface with the intention of going and digging himself a shelter elsewhere. Being unable to do so within the narrow confines of the pot, he stays at the top, barely concealed from view by a modicum of sand or a few scraps of food. A lover of darkness and of the cool underground depths, he remains obstinately for three months exposed to the air and drought and light; he refuses to go to earth, lest he should interfere with the sacred things that are taking place below. The Copris shall have a good mark for thus respecting the maternal apartments.

Let us come back to the jars, where the events hidden from us by the soil are to be enacted before our eyes. The three or four pills, each with its egg, stand one against another and occupy almost the whole enclosure, leaving only narrow passages. Of the original lump very little remains, at the most a few crumbs, which come in handy when appetite returns. But that does not worry the mother much. She is far more concerned about her ovoids.

Assiduously she goes from one to another, feels them, listens to them, touches them up at points where my eye can perceive no flaw. Her clumsy, horn-shod foot, more sensitive in darkness than my retina in broad daylight, is perhaps discovering incipient cracks or defective workmanship in the matter of consistency which must be attended to, in order to prevent the air from entering and drying up the eggs. The prudent mother therefore slips in and out of the narrow spaces between the cradles, inspecting them carefully and remedying any accident, no matter how trifling. If I disturb her, she sometimes rubs the tip of her abdomen against the edge of her wing-cases, producing a soft rustling noise, which is almost a murmur of complaint. Thus, between scrupulous care and brief slumbers beside her group of cradles, the mother passes the three months essential to the evolution of the family.

I seem to catch a glimpse of the reason for this long watch. The pill-rollers, whether Scarabs or Gymnopleuri, never have more than a single pear, a single ovoid in their burrows. The mass of foodstuff, which at times is rolled from a great distance, is necessarily limited by the insect's own limitations of strength. It is enough for one larva, but not enough for two. An exception must be made with respect to the Broad-necked Scarab, who brings up her family very frugally and divides her rolling booty into two modest portions.

The others are obliged to dig a special burrow for each egg. When everything is in order in the new establishment—and this does not take long—they leave the underground vault and go off somewhere else, wherever chance may lead them, to begin their pill-rolling, excavating and egg-laying once more. With these nomadic habits, any prolonged supervision on the mother's part becomes impossible.

The Scarab suffers by it. Her pear, which is magnificently regular at the outset, soon shows cracks and becomes scaly and swollen. Various cryptogams invade it and undermine it; the material expands and the resultant splitting causes the pear to lose its shape. We have seen how the grub combats these troubles.

The Copris has other ways. She does not roll her stores from a distance; she warehouses them on the spot, bit by bit, which enables her to accumulate in a single burrow enough to satisfy all her brood. As there is no need for further expeditions, the mother stays and keeps watch. Under her never-failing vigilance, the pill does not crack, for any crevice is stopped up as soon as it appears; nor does it become covered with parasitic vegetation, for nothing can grow on a soil that is constantly being raked. The two or three dozen ovoids which I have before my eyes all bear witness to the mother's watchfulness: not one of them is split or cracked or infested with tiny fungi. In all of them the surface is irreproachable. But, if I take them away from the mother to put them into a bottle or tin, they suffer the same fate as the Sacred Beetle's pears: in the absence of supervision, destruction more or less complete overtakes them.

Two examples will be instructive to us here. I take from a mother two or three pills and place them in a tin, which prevents them from getting dry. Before a week has passed, they are covered with a fungous vegetation. More or less everything grows in this fertile soil; the lesser fungi delight in it. To-day it is an infinitesimal crystalline plant swollen into a bobbin-shape, bristling with short, dew-beaded hairs and ending in a little round head as black as jet. I have not the leisure to consult books and microscope and give a name to the tiny apparition which attracts my attention for the first time. This botanical detail is of little importance: all that we need know is that the dark green of the pills has disappeared under the thick white crystalline growth stippled with black specks.

I restore the two pills to the Copris keeping watch over her third. I replace the opaque sheath and leave the insect undisturbed in the dark. In an hour's time or less, I look to see how things are getting on. The parasitic vegetation has entirely disappeared, cut down, extirpated to the last stalk. The magnifying-glass fails to reveal a trace of what, a little while before, was a dense thicket. The insect has used its rake, those notched legs, to some purpose; and the surface of the pill is once more in the unblemished condition necessary for health.

The other experiment is a more serious one. With the point of my penknife I make a gash in a pill at the upper end and lay bare the egg. Here we have an artificial breach not unlike those which might be caused naturally, but of much greater size. I give back to the mother the violated cradle, threatened with disaster unless she intervenes. But she does intervene and that quickly, once darkness comes. The ragged edges slit by the penknife are brought together and soldered. The small amount of stuff lost is replaced by scrapings taken from the sides. In a very short time the breach is so neatly repaired that not a trace remains of my onslaught.

I repeat it, making the danger graver and attacking all four pills with my desecrating penknife, which cuts right through the hatching-chamber and leaves the egg only an incomplete shelter under the gaping roof. The mother's counter-move is swift and effective. In one brief spell of work everything is put right again. Yes, I can quite believe that with this vigilant supervisor, who never sleeps except with one eye open, there is no possibility of the cracks and the puffiness which so often disfigure the Sacred Beetle's pear.

Four pills containing eggs are all that I have been able to obtain from the big loaf which I took from the burrow at the time of the nuptials. Does this mean that the Copris can lay only that number? I think so. I even believe that usually there are less, three, two, or possibly only one. My boarders, installed in separate potfuls of sand at nesting-time, did not reappear on the surface once they had stored away the necessary provisions; they never came out to dip into the replenished stock and enable themselves to increase the always restricted number of ovoids lying at the bottom of the pot under the mother's watchful care.

This limitation of the family might very well be due partly to lack of space. Three or four pills completely fill the burrow; there is no room for more; and the mother, a stay-at-home alike from duty and inclination, does not dream of digging another dwelling. It is true that greater breadth in the one which she has would solve the problem of room; but then a ceiling of excessive length would be liable to collapse. Suppose I were myself to intervene, suppose I provided space without the risk of the roof falling in, could there be an increase in the number of eggs?

Yes, the number is almost doubled. My trick is quite simple. In one of the glass jars, I take away her three or four pills from a mother who has just finished the last. None of the loaf remains. I substitute for it one of my own making, kneaded with the tip of a paper-knife. A new type of baker, I do over again very nearly what the insect did at the beginning. Reader, do not smile at my baking: science shall give it the odour of sanctity.

My cake is favourably received by the Copris, who sets to work again, starts laying anew and presents me with three of her perfect ovoids, making seven in all, the greatest number that I obtained in my various attempts of this kind. A large piece of the bun remains available. The Copris does not utilize it, at least not for nest-building; she eats it. The ovaries appear to be exhausted. This much is proved: the pillaging of the burrow provides space; and the mother, taking advantage of it, nearly doubles the number of her eggs with the aid of the cake which I make for her.

Under natural conditions nothing of a similar kind can happen. There is no obliging baker at hand, to shape and pat a new cake and slip it into the oven that is the Copris' cellar. Everything therefore tells us that the stay-at-home Beetle, who makes up her mind not to reappear until the cool autumn days, is of very limited bearing-capacity. Her family consists of three or four at most. Occasionally, in the dog-days, long after laying-time is past, I have even dug up a mother watching over a solitary pill. This one, perhaps for lack of provisions, had reduced her maternal joys to the narrowest limits.

The loaves kneaded with my paper-knife are readily accepted. We will take advantage of this fact to make a few experiments. Instead of the big, substantial cake, I fashion a pill which is a replica in shape and size of the three or four which the mother is guarding after confiding the egg to them. My imitation is a fairly good one. If I were to mix up the two products, the natural and the artificial, I might easily fail to distinguish between them afterwards. The counterfeit pill is placed in the jar, beside the other. The disturbed insect at once hides in a corner, under a little sand. I leave it in peace for a couple of days. Then how great is my surprise to find the mother on the top of my pill, digging a cup into it! In the afternoon the egg is laid and the cup closed. I can only tell my pill from those of the Copris by the place which it occupies. I had put it at the extreme right of the group, and at the extreme right I find it, duly operated on by the insect. How could the Beetle know that this ovoid, so like the others in every respect, was untenanted? How did she allow herself unhesitatingly to scoop the top into a crater when, judging by appearances, there might be an egg just underneath? She takes good care not to do any fresh excavating on the finished pills. What guide leads her to the artificial one, which is extremely deceptive in appearance, and bids her dig into that?

I do it again and yet again. The result is the same: the mother does not confuse her work with mine and takes advantage of the presence of my pill to install an egg in it. On only one occasion, when her appetite seems suddenly to have come back, did I see her feeding on my loaf. But her discrimination between the tenanted and the untenanted was just as clearly marked here as in the previous instance. Instead of attacking, in her hunger, the pills with eggs, by what miracle of divination does she turn, in spite of their exact outward similarity, to the pill which contains nothing?

Can my handiwork be defective? Did the wooden blade not press hard enough to impart the proper consistency? Is there something wrong with the dough as the result of insufficient kneading? These are delicate questions, of which I, who am no expert in this kind of confectionery, am not competent to judge. Let us have recourse to a master of the pastry-cook's art. I borrow from the Sacred Beetle the pill which he is beginning to roll in the vivarium. I choose a small one, of the size affected by the Copris. True, it is round; but the Copris' pills also are pretty often round, even after receiving the egg.

Well, the Sacred Beetle's loaf, that loaf of irreproachable quality, kneaded by the king of bread-makers, meets with the same fate as mine. At one time it is provided with an egg, at another it is eaten, while no accident ever happens by inadvertence to the exactly similar pills kneaded by the Copris.

That the insect, finding itself in this mixed assembly, should rip open what is still inanimate matter and respect what is already a cradle, that it should discriminate between the lawful and the unlawful, in circumstances such as these, seems to me incapable of explanation, if there be no guide but senses resembling our own. It is useless to say that it is a case of sight: the Beetle works in absolute darkness. Even if she worked in the light, that would not lessen the difficulty. The shape and appearance of the pill are alike in both instances; the clearest sight would be at fault once the pills were mixed up.

It is impossible to suggest that smell has anything to do with it: the substance of the pill does not vary; it is always the produce of the Sheep. Impossible likewise to say that she is exercising the sense of touch. What delicacy of touch can there be under a coat of horn? Besides, the most exquisite sensitiveness would be required. Even if we admit that the insect's feet, particularly the tarsi, or the palpi, or the antennæ, or anything you please, possess a certain faculty for distinguishing between hard and soft, rough and smooth, round and angular, still our experiment with the Sacred Beetle's sphere warns us to look where we are going. There surely we had the exact equivalent of the Copris' sphere—made of the same materials, kneaded to the same consistency, given the same outline—and yet the Copris makes no mistake.

To drag the sense of taste into the problem would be absurd. There remains that of hearing. Later on, I might not deny the possibility that this has something to do with it. When the larva is hatched, the mother, ever attentive, might conceivably hear it nibbling the wall of the cell, but for the present the chamber contains merely an egg; and an egg is always silent.

Then what other means does the mother possess, I will not say of thwarting my machinations—the problem is on a loftier plane and animals are not endowed with special aptitudes in order to dodge an experimenter's wiles—what other means does she possess of obviating the difficulties attendant upon her normal labours? Do not lose sight of this: she begins by shaping a sphere; and the globular mass often does not differ from the pills that have received the egg, in respect of either form or size.

Nowhere is there peace, not even below ground. When, in a moment of panic, the too-timid mother falls off her sphere and forsakes it to seek refuge elsewhere, how can she afterwards find her ball again and distinguish it from the others, without running the risk of crushing an egg when she is pressing in the top of a pill to make the necessary crater? She needs a safe guide here. What is that guide? I do not know.

I have said it many a time and I say it again: insects possess sense-faculties of exquisite delicacy attuned to their special trade, faculties of which we can form no conception because we have nothing similar within ourselves. A man blind from birth can have no notion of colour. We are as men blind from birth in the face of the unfathomable mysteries that surround us; and myriads of questions arise to which no answer can ever be given.

CHAPTER X
THE SPANISH COPRIS: THE HABITS OF THE MOTHER

There are two special points to be remembered in the life-history of the Spanish Copris: the rearing of her family; and her pill-rolling talents.

First, the output of her ovaries is extremely limited; and nevertheless her race thrives just as much as that of many others whose seed is numerous. Maternal care makes up for the small number of her eggs. Prolific layers, after making a few rough and ready arrangements, abandon their progeny to luck, which often sacrifices a thousand in order to preserve one; they are factories turning out organic matter for life's comprehensive maw. Almost as soon as hatched, or even before hatching, their offspring for the most part perish devoured. Extermination makes short work of superfluity in the interests of the community at large. That which was destined to live lives, but under another form. These excessive breeders know and can know nothing of maternal affection.

The Copres have other and fundamentally different habits. Three or four eggs represent their entire posterity. How are they to be preserved, to a great extent, from the accidents that await them? For them, so few in numbers, as for the others, whose name is legion, existence is an inexorable struggle. The mother knows it and, in order to save her nearest and dearest, sacrifices herself, giving up outdoor pleasures, nocturnal flights and that supreme delight of her race, the investigation of a fresh heap of dung. Hidden underground, by the side of her brood, she never leaves her nursery. She keeps watch; she brushes off the parasitic growths; she closes up the cracks; she drives off any ravagers that may appear: Acari,1 tiny Staphylini,2 grubs of small Flies, Aphodii,3 Onthophagi.4 In September she climbs to the surface with her family, which, having no further use for her, emancipates itself and henceforth lives as it pleases. No bird could be a more devoted mother.

Secondly, the Copris' abrupt transformation at laying-time into an expert pill-maker provides us, in so far as we are able to get at the truth, with a proof of the theorem which I was almost afraid to formulate just now. Here is a Beetle not equipped for the pill-roller's art, an art moreover which is not required for her individual prosperity. She has no aptitude, no propensity for kneading the food which she buries and consumes as she finds it; she is totally ignorant of the sphere and its properties in connection with food-preservation; and, all of a sudden, in obedience to an inspiration for which nothing, in the ordinary course of her life, has prepared the way, she moulds into a sphere or ovoid the legacy which she bequeaths to her grub. With her short, clumsy fore-leg she shapes the viaticum of her offspring into a skilful solid mass. The difficulty is great. It is overcome by dint of application and patience. In two days, or three at most, the round cradle is perfected. How does the dumpy creature go to work to achieve mathematical exactness in her ball? The Sacred Beetle has her long legs, which serve as compasses; the Gymnopleurus has similar tools. But the Copris, unprovided with the spread of limb which would enable her to encircle the object, finds nothing in her equipment that favours the formation of a sphere. Perched upon her ovoid, she labours at it bit by bit with an intensity that makes up for her defective implements; she estimates the correctness of its curve by assiduous tactile examinations from one end to the other. Perseverance triumphs over clumsiness and achieves what at first seemed impossible.

Here all my readers will assail me with the same questions: why this abrupt change in the insect's habits? Why this indefatigable patience in a form of work that bears no relation to the tools at hand? And what is the use of this ovoid shape whose perfection demands so great an outlay of time?

To these queries I see only one possible reply: the preservation of the foodstuffs in a fresh condition demands the globular form. Remember this: the Copris builds her nest in June; her larva develops during the dog-days; it lies a few inches below the surface of the ground. In the cavern, which is now a furnace, the provisions would soon become uneatable, if the mother did not give them the shape least susceptible to evaporation. Very different from the Sacred Beetle in habits and structure but exposed to the same dangers in her larval state, the Copris, in order to ward off the peril, adopts the principles of the great pill-roller, principles whose surpassing wisdom we have already made manifest.

I would ask the philosophers to ponder upon these five manufacturers of preserved meats and the numerous rivals which they doubtless possess in other climes. I submit to them these inventors of the largest possible box with the smallest possible surface for provisions liable to dry; and I ask them how such logical inspirations and so much rational foresight can take birth in the obscure brain of the lower orders of creation.

Let us come down to plain facts. The Copris' pill is a more or less pronounced ovoid, sometimes differing but slightly from a sphere in shape. It is not quite so pretty as the work of the Gymnopleurus, which is very nearly pear-shaped, or at least reminds one of a bird's egg, notably a

Sparrow's, because of the similarity in size. The Copris' work is more like the egg of a nocturnal bird of prey, of any member of the Owl family, as its projecting end does not stand out conspicuously.

From this pole to the other the ovoid measures, on an average, forty millimetres, by thirty-four across.5 Its whole surface is tightly packed, hardened by pressure, converted into a crust with a little earth grained into it. At the projecting end, an attentive eye will discover a ring bristling with short straggling threads. Once the egg is laid in the cup into which the original sphere is hollowed, the mother, as I have already said, gradually brings the edges of the cavity together. This produces the projecting end. To complete the closing, she delicately rakes the ovoid and scrapes a little of the material upwards. This forms the ceiling of the hatching-chamber. At the top of this ceiling, which, if it fell in, would destroy the egg, the pressure is very slight indeed, leaving an area devoid of rind and covered with bits of thread. Immediately under this circle, which is a sort of porous felt, lies the hatching-chamber, the egg's little cell, which easily admits air and warmth.

Like the Sacred Beetle's egg and those of other Dung-beetles, the Copris' egg at once attracts attention by its size, but it grows much larger before hatching, increasing two- or threefold in bulk. Its moist chamber, saturated with the emanations from the provisions, supplies it with nourishment. Through the chalky porous shell of the bird's egg, an exchange of gases takes place, a respiratory process which quickens matter while consuming it. This is a cause of destruction as well as of life: the sum total of the contents does not increase under the inflexible wrapper; on the contrary, it diminishes.

Things happen otherwise in the Copris' egg, as in the other Dung-beetles'. We still, no doubt, find the vivifying assistance of the air; but there is also an accession of new materials which come to add to the reserves furnished by the ovary. Endosmosis causes the exhalations of the chamber to penetrate through a very delicate membrane, so much so that the egg is fed, swells and enlarges to thrice its original volume. If we have failed to follow this progressive growth attentively, we are quite surprised at the extraordinary final size, which is out of all proportion to that of the mother.

This nourishment lasts a fairly long time, for the hatching takes from fifteen to twenty days. Thanks to the added substance with which the egg has been enriched, the larva is already pretty big when born. We have not here the weakly grub, the animated speck which many insects show us, but a pretty little creature, at once sturdy and tender, which, happy at being alive, arches its back and frisks and rolls about in its nest.

It is satin-white, with a touch of straw-colour on its skull-cap. I find the terminal trowel plainly marked: I mean that slanting plane with the scalloped edge whereof the Sacred Beetle has already shown us the use when some breach in the cell needs repairing. The implement tells us the future trade. You also, my attractive little grub, will become a knapsacked excreter, a fervent plasterer manipulating the stucco supplied by the intestines. But first I will subject you to an experiment.

Now what are your first mouthfuls? As a rule I see the walls of your nest shining with a greenish, semifluid wash, a sort of thinly-spread jam. Is this a special dish intended for your delicate baby stomach? Is it a childish dainty disgorged by the mother? I used to think so when I first began to study the Sacred Beetle. To-day, after seeing a similar wash in the cells of the various Dung-beetles, including the uncouth Geotrupes,6 I wonder whether it is not rather the result of a mere exudation accumulating on the walls in a sort of dew, the fluid quintessence filtering through the porous matter.

The Copris mother lent herself to observation better than any of the others. I have many times surprised her at the moment when, hoisted on her round pill, she excavates the top in the form of a cup; and I have never seen anything that at all suggests a disgorgement. The cavity of the bowl, which I lose no time in examining, is just like the rest. Perhaps I have missed the favourable moment. In any case, I can take only a brief glance at the mother's occupations: all work ceases as soon as I raise the cardboard sheath to give light. Under these conditions the secret might escape me indefinitely. Let us look at the difficulty from another angle and enquire whether some special milk-food, elaborated in the mother's stomach, is necessary for the infant larva.

In one of my cages I rob a Sacred Beetle of her round pill, lately fashioned and briskly rolled. I strip it at one point of its earthy layer and into this clean point I drive the blunt end of a pencil, making a hole a third of an inch deep. I install a newly-hatched Copris-grub in it. The youngster has not yet taken the least refreshment. It is lodged in a cell which in no respect differs from the rest of the mass. There is no creamy coating, whether disgorged by the mother or merely oozing through. What will result from this change of quarters?

Nothing untoward. The larva develops and thrives quite as well as in its native cell. Therefore, when I first started, I was the victim of an illusion. The delicate wash which nearly always covers the egg-chamber in the Dung-beetles' work is simply an exudation. The grub may be all the better for it, when taking its first mouthfuls; but it is not indispensable. To-day's experiment confirms the fact.

The grub subjected to this test was put into an open pit. Things cannot remain in this condition. The absence of ceiling is irksome to the young larva, which loves darkness and tranquillity. How will it set to work to build its roof? The mortar-trowel cannot be used as yet, for materials are lacking in the knapsack which so far has done no digesting.

Novice though it be, the little grub has its resources. Since it cannot be a plasterer, it becomes a bricklayer. With its legs and mandibles it removes particles from the walls of its cell and comes and places them one by one on the rim of the well. The defensive work makes rapid progress and the assembled atoms form a vault. It has no strength about it, I admit; the dome falls in if I merely breathe on it. But soon the first mouthfuls will be swallowed; the intestines will fill; and, well supplied, the grub will come and consolidate the work by injecting mortar into the interstices. Properly cemented, the frail awning becomes a solid ceiling.

Let us leave the tiny grub in peace and consult other larvæ which have attained half their full growth. With the point of my penknife I pierce the pill at the upper end; I open a window a few millimetres square. The grub at once appears at the casement, anxiously enquiring into the disaster. It rolls itself over in the cell and returns to the opening, this time, however, presenting its wide, padded trowel. A jet of mortar is discharged over the breach. The product is a little too much diluted and of inferior quality. It runs, it flows in all directions, it does not set quickly. A fresh ejaculation follows and another and yet another, in swift succession. Useless pains! In vain the plasterer tries again, in vain it struggles, gathering the trickling material with its legs and mandibles: the hole refuses to close. The mortar is still too fluid.

Poor, desperate thing, why don't you copy your young sister? Do what the little larva did just now: build an awning with particles taken from the wall of your house; and your liquid putty will do well on that spongy scaffolding! The large grub, trusting to its trowel, does not think of that method. It exhausts itself, without any appreciable result, in trying to effect repairs which the little grub managed most ingeniously. What the baby knew how to do the big larva no longer knows.

Insect industry has instances like this of professional methods employed at certain periods and then abandoned and utterly forgotten. A few days more or less make changes in the creature's talents. The tiny grub, devoid of cement, has bricks to fall back upon: the big larva, rich in putty, scorns to build, or rather no longer knows how, though it is even better-endowed than the youngster with the necessary tools. The strong one no longer remembers what as a weakling he so well knew how to do, only a few days before. A poor power of recollection, if indeed there be such a power under that flat skull! However, in the long run and thanks to the evaporation of the ejected materials, the short-memoried plumber ends by stopping up the window. Nearly half a day has been spent in trowel-work.

The idea occurs to me to try whether the mother will come to the distressed one's aid in like circumstances. We have seen her diligently restoring the ceiling which I smashed above the egg. Will she do for the big grub what she did for the sake of the germ? Will she repair the torn pill in which the plasterer is helplessly floundering?

To make the experiment more conclusive, I select pills that do not belong to the mother entrusted with the work of restoration. I picked them up in the fields. They are far from regular, are all dented because of the stony soil on which they lay, a soil not easily convertible into a roomy workshop and consequently unsuited to exact geometry. They are moreover encrusted with a reddish rind, due to the ferruginous sand in which I packed them in order to avoid dangerous jolting on the road. In short, they differ a good deal from those elaborated in a jar, with plenty of space around them and on a clean support, pills which are perfect ovoids, free from earthy stains. In the top of two of them I make an opening which the grub, faithful to its methods, at once strives to stop up, but without success. One, stored away under a bell-glass, will serve me as a witness. The other I place in a jar where the mother is watching her cradles, two splendid ovoids.

I have not long to wait. An hour later I raise the cardboard screen. The Copris is on the strange pill and so busily engaged that she pays no attention to the daylight admitted. In other, less urgent circumstances, she would at once have slipped down and taken shelter from the troublesome light; this time, she does not move and imperturbably continues her work. Before my eyes she rakes away the red crust and uses the scrapings from the cleansed surface to spread over and solder the breach. It is hermetically sealed in a very short space of time. I stand amazed at the insect's skill.

Well, while the Copris is restoring a pill that does not belong to her, what is the grub that owns the other doing in the bell-glass? It continues to kick about hopelessly, vainly lavishing cement that is incapable of setting. Put to the test in the morning, it does not succeed until the afternoon in closing the aperture; and then the job is anything but well done. The borrowed mother, on the other hand, has not taken twenty minutes to remedy the accident most excellently.

She does even more. After the most important part is finished and the afflicted grub succoured, she stands all day, all night and the next day on the newly-closed pill. She brushes it daintily with her tarsi to get rid of the layer of earth; she obliterates the dents, smooths the rough places and adjusts the curve, until from a shapeless and soiled pill it becomes an ovoid vying in precision with those which she had already manufactured in her glass jar.

Such care bestowed upon a strange grub deserves attention. I must go on. I slip into the jar a second pill, similar to the foregoing, ruptured at the top, with an opening larger than on the first occasion, one about a sixteenth of an inch square. The greater the difficulty, the more praiseworthy will the restoration be.

It is, indeed, difficult to close. The grub, a fat baby, is wildly gesticulating and excreting through the window. Leaning over the hole, its new mother seems to console it. She is like a nurse bending over the cradle. Meanwhile her helpful legs are working with a will, scratching around the yawning aperture to obtain the wherewithal to stop it. But the materials, half-dried this time, are hard and unyielding. They are slow in coming; and the quantity is too small for so big a hole. No matter: what with the grub continuing to shoot forth its putty and the other mixing it with her own scrapings, to give it consistency, and afterwards spreading it, the opening closes up.

The thankless task has taken a whole afternoon. It is a good lesson for me. I shall be more careful in future. I shall choose softer pills and, instead of opening them by removing the materials, I shall simply lift the wall by shreds until the grub is laid bare. The mother will only have to flatten down those shreds and solder them together.

I act accordingly with a third pill, which is very neatly repaired in a short time. Not a trace remains of the ravages caused by my penknife. I continue in the same way with a fourth, a fifth and so on, at intervals long enough to give the mother a rest. I stop when the receptacle is full, looking like a pot of plums. The contents amount to twelve pieces, of which ten have come from the outside, all ten violated by my penknife and all restored to good condition by the foster-mother.

There are some interesting sidelights to this curious experiment, which I could have continued if the capacity of the jar had permitted. The Copris' zeal, which was not lessened after the restoring of so many ruins, and her diligence, which was the same at the end as in the beginning, tell me that I had not exhausted the maternal solicitude. Let us leave it at that; it is amply sufficient.

Observe first the arrangement of the pills. Three are enough to occupy the floor-space of the enclosure. The others are therefore gradually superposed in layers, making in the end a four-story structure. The whole forms an irregular pile, an absolute labyrinth with very narrow, winding lanes, through which the insect glides with some difficulty. When her household is in order, the mother stays below, under the pile, touching the sand. It is at this moment that a new broken cell is introduced, right at the top of the pile, on the third or fourth floor. Let us put back the screen, wait a few minutes and then go back to the jar.

The mother is there, hoisted on the torn pill and doing her utmost to close it. How was she informed on the ground-floor of what was happening in the attic? How did she know that a larva up there was calling for her assistance? The babe in distress screams and the nurse comes running up. The grub says nothing; it makes no sound. Its desperate gesticulations are not accompanied by any noise. And the watcher hears this mute appeal. She notices the silence, she sees the invisible. I am bewildered, every one would be bewildered by the mystery of these perceptions which are so foreign to our nature and which 'topsy turvy the understanding,' as Montaigne would say. Let us pass on.

I have described elsewhere7 the brutality with which the Bee, that most gifted of insects, treats the eggs of her fellows. Osmiæ, Chalicodomæ and others perpetrate atrocities at times. In a moment of vengeance or of that inexplicable aberration which occurs after the laying is finished, a sister's egg, savagely torn from the cell with the pincers of the mandibles, is flung into the dust-bin. The thing is pitilessly crushed, is ripped open, is even eaten. How different from the good-natured Copris!

Shall we attribute altruism among families to the Dung-beetle? Shall we do her the signal honour of allowing that she administers relief to foundlings? That would be madness. The mother who so diligently assists the children of others thinks, beyond a doubt, that she is working for her own. The victim of my experiment had two pills that belonged to her; my intervention gave her ten more. And, in the jar filled with prunes to the top, her assiduous care draws no distinction between the real household and the casual family. Her intellect therefore is incapable of the most elementary conception of quantity; she cannot even distinguish between the singular and the plural, the few and the many.

Can it be because of the darkness? No, for my frequent visits give the Copris an opportunity, when the opaque screen is lifted, of looking around her and discovering the strange accumulation, that is if light be really the guide which she lacks. Besides, has she not another means of information? In the natural burrow, the pills, three or at most four in number, all lie on the ground, forming one row only. With my additions they pile up into four stories.

In order to clamber to the top, in order to hoist herself up through such a maze as never Copris mansion knew before, the Beetle must rub against and touch the units of the heap. But she counts none the better for that. To the insect all this is just the home, is just the family, worthy of the same care at the summit as at the base. The twelve produced by my trickery and the two of her own laying are the same thing in her arithmetic.

I present this strange mathematician to any one who comes and talks to me of a glimmer of reason in the insect, as Darwin claimed. It is one of two things: either this glimmer does not exist, or else the Copris reasons divinely and becomes a St. Vincent de Paul of insects, moved to pity by the sad lot of the homeless. Make your choice.

It is possible that, rather than abandon the principle, men will not shrink from sheer folly and that the compassionate Copris will one day figure in the evolutionists' Book of Moral Deeds. Why not? Does it not already, with an eye to the same argument, contain a certain tender-hearted Boa Constrictor who, on losing his master, lay down and died of grief? Oh, the fond reptile! These edifying stories, compiled with the object of tracing man back to the Gorilla, procure me a few moments of mild amusement when I come across them. But we will not labour the point.

Better that you and I, friend Copris, should speak of things that do not raise storms. Would you mind telling me the reason of the reputation which you enjoyed in the days of antiquity? Ancient Egypt extolled you in pink granite and porphyry; she venerated you, O my fair horned one, and awarded you honours similar to the Scarab's! You ranked second in the entomological hierarchy.

Horapollo tells us of two Sacred Beetles with horns. One sported a single specimen on her head, the other had two. The first is you, the inmate of my glass jars, or at least some one very like you. If Egypt had known what you have just taught me, she would certainly have placed you above the Scarab, that roving pill-roller who deserts her home and leaves her family, after it has received its inheritance, to shift for itself as best it can. Knowing nothing of your wonderful habits, which history is noting for the first time, she deserves all the greater praise for having divined your merits.

The second, the one with two horns, would, according to the experts, appear to be the insect which the naturalists call the Isis Copris. I know her only in effigy, but her image is so striking that I sometimes catch myself dreaming late in life, just as I did in my youth, of going down to Nubia and exploring the banks of the Nile, in order to cross-examine, under some lump of Camel-dung, the insect that is emblematic of Isis the divine brooder, nature made fruitful by Osiris, the sun.

Oh, simpleton! Attend to your cabbages, sow your turnips: that won't do you any harm; water your lettuces; and understand, once and for all, how vain are all our questionings when it is simply a matter of enquiring into a muck-raker's sagacity! Be less ambitious; confine yourself to setting down facts.

So be it. There is nothing striking to be said of the larva, which is a replica of the Sacred Beetle's, save for some minute details which do not interest us here. It has the same hump in the middle of its back, the same slanting truncature of the last segment, expanding into a trowel on the upper surface. A ready excreter, it understands, though less thoroughly than the other, the art of stopping up breaches to protect itself from draughts. The larval state covers a period of four to six weeks.

At the end of July the nymph appears, first amber-yellow all over, next currant-red on the head, horn, corselet, breast and legs, while the wing-cases have the pale hue of gum arabic. A month later, by the end of August, the perfect insect releases itself from its mummy wrappers. Its costume, now wrought upon by delicate chemical changes, is quite as strange as that of the new-born Sacred Beetle. Head, corselet, breast and legs are chestnut-red. The horn, the epistoma and the denticulations of the fore-legs are shaded with brown. The wing-cases are a rather yellowish white. The abdomen is white, excepting only the anal segment, which is an even brighter red than the thorax. I perceive this early colouring of the anal segment, while the rest of the abdomen is still quite pale, in the Sacred Beetles, the Gymnopleuri, the Onthophagi, the Geotrupes, the Cetoniæ8 and many others. Whence this precocity? One more note of interrogation which will long stand awaiting a reply.

A fortnight passes. The costume becomes ebon-black, the cuirass hardens. The insect is ready for the emergence. We are at the end of September; the earth has drunk in a few showers which soften the stubborn shell and allow of an easy deliverance. This is the moment, prisoners mine. If I have teased you a little, at least I have kept you in plenty. Your shells have hardened in your cages and have become caskets which your own efforts will never succeed in forcing open. I will come to your aid. Let us describe in detail how things happen.

Once the burrow is supplied with the voluminous loaf out of which three or four pilular rations are to be carved, the mother does not appear outside again. Besides, there is no provision made for her. The heap stored away below is the family cake, the exclusive patrimony of the grubs, who will receive equal shares. For four months, therefore, the recluse is without food of any kind.

It is a voluntary privation. Victuals are there, within reach, copious and of superior quality; but they are intended for the larvæ and the mother will take good care not to touch them: anything abstracted for her own use would mean so much less for the grubs. Gluttonous at the outset, when there was no family to consider, she now becomes very abstemious, even to the point of prolonged fasting. The Hen sitting on her eggs forgets to eat for some weeks; the watchful Copris mother forgets it during a third part of the year. The Dung-beetle outdoes the bird in maternal self-abnegation.

Now what does this self-sacrificing mother do underground? To what household cares can she devote the period of so long a fast? My appliances provide a satisfactory answer. I possess, as I have said, two kinds. One consists of glass jars with a thin layer of sand and a cardboard case to create darkness; the other of large pots filled with earth and closed with a pane of glass.

At any moment when I raise the opaque sheath of the first, I find the mother now perched upon the top of her ovoids, now on the ground, half-erect, smoothing the bulging curve with her fore-leg. On rarer occasions, she is dozing in the midst of the heap.

The manner in which she employs her time is obvious. She watches her treasure of pills; her inquisitive antennæ sound them to discover what is happening inside; she listens to the nurselings growing; she touches up faulty spots; she polishes and repolishes the surfaces in order to delay the desiccation within until the development of the inmates is complete.

These scrupulous cares, cares occupying every moment, have results which would strike the attention of the least-experienced observer. The egg-shaped vessels, or better the cradles of the nursery, are wonderful in their regular curves and in their neatness. We see none of those chinks with a blob of putty showing through, none of those cracks, of those peeling scales, in short none of those defects which, towards the end, nearly always disfigure the Sacred Beetle's pears, handsome though they be at the start.

The horned Dung-beetle's caskets could not be better shaped, even after they are thoroughly dried up, if they had been worked in plaster by a modeller. What pretty, dark-bronze eggs they are, rivalling the Owl's in size and form! This irreproachable perfection, maintained until the shell is burst by the emerging larva, is obtained only by incessant touching up, interspersed at long intervals with periods of rest during which the mother composes herself for a nap at the foot of the heap.

The glass jars leave room for doubt. It is possible to say that the insect, imprisoned in an impassable enclosure, stays in the midst of its pills because it is unable to go elsewhere. I agree; but there remains that work of polishing and of continual inspection about which the mother need not trouble at all if these cares did not form part of her habits. Were she solely anxious to recover her liberty, she ought to be roaming restlessly all round the enclosure, whereas I always see her very quiet and absorbed. The only evidence of her excitement, when the raising of the cardboard cylinder suddenly produces daylight, is that she lets herself slide from the top of a pill and hides in the heap. If I moderate the light, composure is soon restored and she resumes her position on the summit, there to continue the work which my visit interrupted.

For the rest, the evidence of the apparatus that is always in darkness is conclusive. The mother buried herself in June in the sand of my pots with copious provisions, which are soon converted into a certain number of pills. She is at liberty to return to the surface when she pleases. She will there find broad daylight under the big sheet of glass which ensures me against her escape; she will find food, which I renew from time to time in order to entice her.

Well, neither the daylight nor the food, desirable though this must seem to be after a fast so long extended, is able to tempt her. Nothing stirs in my pots, nothing rises to the surface until the rains come.

It is exceedingly probable that exactly the same thing happens underground as in the jars. To make certain, I inspect some of my appliances at different periods. I always find the mother beside her pills, in a spacious cave which gives free play to the watcher's evolutions. She could go lower down in the sand and hide anywhere she pleased, if rest is what she wants; she could climb outside and sit down to fresh victuals, if refreshment became necessary. Neither the prospects of rest in a deeper crypt nor the thought of the sun and of nice soft rolls make her leave her family. Until the last of her offspring has burst his shell, she sticks to her post in the birth-chamber.

It is now October. The rains so greatly desired by man and beast have come at last, soaking the ground to some depth. After the torrid and dusty days of summer, when life is in suspense, we have the coolness that revives it, we have the last festival of the year. In the midst of the heath putting out its first pink bells, the *oronge* 9 splits its white purse and comes into view, looking like the yolk of an egg half deprived of its albumen; the massive purple boletus turns blue under the heel of the passer-by who crushes it; the autumnal squill lifts its little spike of lilac flowers; the strawberry-tree's coral balls begin to soften.

This tardy springtime has its echoes underground. The vernal generations, Sacred Beetles and Gymnopleuri, Onthophagi and Copres, hasten to burst their shells softened by the damp and come to the surface to take part in the gaieties of the last fine weather.

My captives are denied the friendly shower. The cement of their caskets, baked by the summer heat, is too hard to yield. The file of the shield and legs would make no impression on it. I come to the poor things' assistance. A carefully graduated watering replaces the natural rain in my glass and earthenware pots. To ascertain once more the effects of water on the Dung-beetles' deliverance, I leave a few of the receptacles in the state of dryness for which they have to thank the dog-days.

The result of my sprinkling soon becomes apparent. In a few days' time, now in one jar, now in another, the pills, properly softened, open and fall to pieces under the prisoner's efforts. The new-born Copris appears and sits down, with his mother, to the food which I have placed at his disposal.

When the hermit, stiffening his legs and humping his back, tries to split the ceiling that presses down on him, does the mother come to his assistance by delivering an assault from the outside? It is quite possible.

The watcher, hitherto so careful of her brood, so attentive to what is happening within the pills, can hardly fail to hear the sounds made by the captive in his struggles to emerge.

We have seen her indefatigably stopping the holes caused by my indiscretion; we have seen her, often enough, restoring for the grub's greater safety the pill which I had opened with my penknife. Fitted by instinct for repairing and building, why should she not be fitted for demolishing? However, I will make no assertions, for I have been unable to see. The favourable conditions always escaped me: I came either too late or too early. And then let us not forget that the admission of light usually interrupts the work.

In the darkness of the sand-filled pots, the liberation must take place in the same way. All that I am able to witness is the insect's emergence above ground. Attracted by the smell of fresh provisions which I have served on the threshold of the burrow, the newly-released family emerge gradually, accompanied by the mother, wander round for a time under the pane of glass and then attack the pile.

There are three or four of them, five at most. The sons are easily recognized by the greater length of their horns; but there is nothing to distinguish the daughters from the mother. For that matter, the same confusion prevails among themselves. An abrupt change of attitude has taken place; and the erstwhile devoted mother is now utterly indifferent to the welfare of her emancipated family. Henceforward each looks after his own home and his own interests. They no longer know one another.

In the receptacles which are not moistened by artificial showers, things come to a miserable end. The dry shell, almost as hard as an apricot- or peach-stone, offers indomitable resistance. The insect's legs manage to grate off barely so much as a pinch of dust. I hear the tools rasping against the unyielding wall; then silence follows and not a prisoner survives to tell the tale. The mother too perishes in that home which has remained dry when the season for dryness has passed. The Copris, like the Sacred Beetle, needs the rain to soften the granite shell.

To return to the liberated ones. When the emergence is effected, the mother, we were saying, ceases to trouble about them. Her present indifference, however, must not make us forget the wonderful care which she has lavished for four months on end. Outside the Social Hymenoptera—Bees, Wasps, Ants and so on—who spoon-feed their young and bring them up according to scrupulously hygienic methods, where in the insect world shall we find another example of such maternal self-abnegation, of such wise and tender care for the offspring? I know of none.

How did the Copris acquire this lofty quality, which I would readily call a moral quality, if morality and nescience had any point of contact? How did she learn to surpass in tenderness the Bee and the Ant, both so greatly renowned? I say surpass. The mother Bee, indeed, is simply a germ-factory, a prodigiously fertile factory, I admit. She lays eggs; and that is all. The family is brought up by others, real sisters of charity these, vowed to celibacy.

The Copris mother does more in her humble household. Alone and entirely unaided, she provides each of her children with a cake whose crust, hardening and constantly renovated with the maternal trowel, becomes an inviolable cradle. So intense is her affection that she neglects herself to the extent of losing all need for food. Down in a burrow, for four consecutive months, she watches over her brood, attending to the wants of the germ, the grub, the nymph and the perfect insect. She does not return to the glad outer life until all her family are emancipated. Thus do we behold one of the most brilliant manifestations of maternal instinct in a humble dung-eater. The Spirit breatheth where he will.

1 Mites or Ticks.—*Translator's Note.*

2 Rove-beetles.—*Translator's Note.*

3 A genus of Dung-beetles.—*Translator's Note.*

4 Cf. Chapters XI., XVII. and XVIII. of the present volume.—*Translator's Note.*

5 1·56 × 1·32 inches.—*Translator's Note.*

6 Cf. Chapters XII. to XIV. of the present volume.—*Translator's Note.*

7 Cf. *The Mason-bees* and *Bramble-bees and Others*: *passim*.—*Translator's Note.*

8 Rose-chafers.—*Translator's Note.*

9 Or imperial mushroom. For this and the purple boletus, cf. *The Life of the Fly,* by J. Henri Fabre, translated by Alexander Teixeira de Mattos: chap. xviii.—*Translator's Note.*

CHAPTER XI
ONTHOPHAGI AND ONITICELLI

After the notabilities of the Dung-beetle tribe, if we omit the Geotrupes, who belong to a different clan, there remains, within the very limited radius of my observation, the Onthophagus rabble, of which I could gather a dozen different species around my house. What will these small fry teach us?

Even more zealous than their big companions, they are the first that hasten to exploit the heap left by the passing Mule. They come in crowds and stay a long time working under the spread table that gives them shade and coolness. Turn over the heap with your foot. You will be surprised at the swarming population whose presence no outward sign betrayed. The largest are scarce the size of a pea, but some are much smaller still; and these dwarfs are no less busy than the others, no less eager to crumble into dust the filth which, in the interests of the public health, must be cleared away with all speed.

For the more important work of life there is nothing like the humble toilers for realizing vast strength, made up of their joint weaknesses. Swollen by numbers, the next to nothing becomes an enormous total.

Hurrying in detachments at the first news of the event, assisted moreover in their sanitary work by their partners, the Aphodii, who are as weak as they, the tiny Onthophagi soon clear the ground of its dirt. Not that their appetite is equal to the consumption of such plentiful provisions. What food do these pigmies need? A mere atom. But for that atom, selected from among the exudations, search must be made amid the wisps of masticated fodder. Hence, an endless division and dissection of the lump, reducing it to dust which the sun sterilizes and the wind dispels. As soon as the work is done—and very well done—the troop of scavengers goes in search of another refuse-yard. Except for the period of intense cold, which puts a stop to all activity, they are never idle.

And do not run away with the idea that this filthy task entails an inelegant shape and a ragged dress. Our squalor is unknown to the insect. In its world, a navvy dons a sumptuous jerkin; an undertaker decks himself in a triple saffron sash; a wood-cutter works in a velvet coat. In like manner, the Onthophagus has his special gorgeousness. True, the costume is always severe: brown and black are the predominant colours, now dull, now polished as ebony. That is the general groundwork, but how chaste and elegant are the decorative details!

One (*O. lemur*) has wing-cases of a light chestnut colour, with a semicircle of black dots; a second (*O. nuchicornis*) has similar chestnut wing-cases covered with splashes of Indian ink not unlike the square Hebrew characters; a third (*O. Schreberi*), who is a glossy black like that of jet, decks himself with four vermilion cockades; a fourth (*O. furcatus*) lights up the tip of his short wing-cases with a gleam similar to that of dying embers; many (*O. vacca, O. cænobita* and others) have corselets and heads bright with the metal sheen of Florentine bronze.

The graver's work completes the beauty of the dress. Dainty chasing in parallel grooves, delicate embroidery, knotty chaplets are distributed in profusion among nearly all of them. Yes, the little Onthophagi, with their short bodies and their nimble activity, are really pretty to look at.

And then how original are their frontal decorations! These peace-lovers delight in the panoply of war, as though they, the inoffensive ones, thirsted for battle. Many of them crown their heads with threatening horns. Let us mention a couple of the horned ones whose story will occupy us more particularly. I mean, first, the Bull Onthophagus (*O. taurus*), clad in raven black. He wears a pair of long horns, gracefully curved and branching to either side. No pedigree bull, in the Swiss meadows, can match them for curve or elegance. The second is the Forked Onthophagus (*O. furcatus*), who is much smaller. His equipment consists of a fork with three vertical prongs.

There you have the two chief subjects of this brief Onthophagus biography. The others are equally worthy of being chronicled. From first to last, they would all supply us with interesting details, some of them even with peculiarities unknown elsewhere; but we must draw the line somewhere in this multitude, which is difficult to observe in the aggregate. And there is this more serious circumstance, that my choice has not been free: I have had to content myself with the few lucky discoveries made as the result of chance encounters out of doors and with the few successful experiments made in the vivarium.

Two species only, the two which I have named, have proved satisfactory in both directions. Let us watch them at work. They will show us the principal features of the manner of life led by the whole tribe, for they occupy the two extremes of the scale of sizes, the Bull Onthophagus being one of the largest and the Forked Onthophagus one of the smallest.

We will speak first of the nest. Contrary to my expectation, the Onthophagi are indifferent nest-builders. With them we find no spheres rolled joyously in the sunshine, no ovoids manipulated laboriously in an underground workshop. Their business, that of reducing filth to dust, appears to give them so much to do that they have no time left for work demanding prolonged patience. They confine themselves to what is strictly necessary and most rapidly obtained.

A perpendicular well is dug, a couple of inches deep, cylindrical in shape and varying in bore according to the size of the well-sinker. The pit of the Forked Onthophagus has the diameter of a lead-pencil; that of the Bull Onthophagus is twice the width. Right at the bottom are the grub's provisions, plastered against the walls in a tightly-packed heap. The total lack of free space at the sides of the pile shows how the provisioning is done. There is not a sign of a niche, of the least corner that would leave the mother enough liberty of movement to knead and mould her bun. The material therefore is simply pressed down at the bottom of the cylindrical sheath, where it takes the shape of a full thimble.

I dig up some nests of the Forked Onthophagus near the end of July. It is a crude piece of work, which surprises you by its roughness when you think of the neat little worker. Wisps of hay, sticking out anyhow, increase the untidy look of things. The nature of the materials, supplied this time by the Mule, are partly the cause of this ugly appearance.

The length of these nests is fourteen millimetres, the width seven.1 The upper surface is slightly concave, proving that the pressure has been exercised by the mother. The lower end is rounded like the bottom of the well which serves as a mould. I take a needle and with the point of it I pick the rustic structure to pieces. The mass of foodstuff occupies the base, forming the lower two-thirds of the thimble into a compact block; the cell containing the egg is at the top, under a thin, concave lid.

There is nothing fresh about the work of the Bull Onthophagus, which, save for being larger, differs in no way from that of the Forked Onthophagus. I am unacquainted with the insect's *modus operandi*. As regards the inner secrets of nest-building, these dwarfs are as reticent as their big colleagues. One alone satisfied my curiosity, or nearly; and then it was not an Onthophagus but a kindred species, the Yellow-footed Oniticellus (*O. flavipes*).

I capture her in the last week of July, under a heap which a Mule employed in treading out the corn on the thrashing-floor dropped during a rest from work. The thick blanket, transformed by a hot sun into an incomparable incubator, shelters a host of Onthophagi. The Oniticellus is by herself. Her quick retreat down a yawning well attracts my attention. I dig to a depth of about two inches and extract the lady of the house together with her work, the latter in a sadly damaged condition. I can, however, distinguish a sort of bag.

I install the Oniticellus in a tumbler, on a layer of heaped earth, and give her as her nest-building materials what the Sacred Beetles and the Copres prefer, the Sheep's plastic paste. Caught at the moment when she was about to lay, goaded by the irresistible needs of her ovaries, the mother lends herself very obligingly to my wishes. She lays four eggs in three days. This rapidity, which would doubtless be even greater if my curiosity had not disturbed her in her task, is explained by the simplicity of the work.

The mother goes to the lower surface of the stuff which I have supplied and detaches from the central and softest part a slice sufficient for her plans, removing it all in one piece, by means of a circular section. It is the same method as that employed by the Copris taking from her loaf the wherewithal to make a pellet. There is a pit immediately below, dug in advance. The Oniticellus goes down it with her burden.

I wait half an hour, to give the work time to take shape, and then turn the glass upside down, hoping to surprise the mother in her domestic business. The original little lump is now a bag moulded by pressure against the sides of the well. The mother is at the bottom, motionless, bewildered by my disturbing visit and the intrusion of light. To see her working with her forehead and legs in order to spread the matter, crush it and apply it to its earthen sheath seems to me a very difficult thing to do. I abandon the attempt and restore the glass to its first position.

A little later, I make a second examination, when the mother has left her burrow. The work is now finished. The outward form is that of a thimble fifteen millimetres deep by ten wide.2 The flat end has all the appearance of a lid fitted to the opening and carefully soldered on. The rounded lower half of the thimble is full. This is the grub's larder. Above is the hatching-chamber, with the egg sticking up from the floor, fixed perpendicularly by one end.

Great is the danger for the Oniticellus and the Onthophagus, offspring of the dog-days, both of them. Their jar of preserves is greatly restricted in volume. Its shape is in no way calculated to reduce evaporation; it is too near the surface of the soil to escape the dangerous dryness of the air. If the cake should harden, the grub will die, after its abstinence has been prolonged to the utmost limits of endurance.

I place in glass tubes, which will represent the native well, a few Onthophagus- and Oniticellus-thimbles, first contriving an opening in the side which will enable me to see what happens within. I close the tubes with a plug of cotton and keep them in a shady part of my study. Evaporation must be very slight in these impermeable and moreover plugged sheaths. Nevertheless it is enough to produce in a few days a degree of dryness which is fatal to feeding.

I see the starvelings remain motionless, unable to bite into the hateful crust; I see them lose their plumpness, I see them wrinkle and shrivel, and at last, in a fortnight's time, take on all the appearance of death. I replace the dry cotton with wet cotton. The atmosphere in the tubes becomes damp; the thimbles are gradually saturated with the moisture, swell out and soften; and the dying come back to life. They do so to such good purpose that the whole cycle of the metamorphoses is safely accomplished, on condition that the wet cotton be renewed from time to time.

My carefully graduated artificial shower, with its damped cotton to represent the clouds, inspires that return to life. It is like a resurrection. In the normal conditions prevailing in the torrid, rain-grudging month of August, the probability of an equivalent of that shower is almost *nil*. How then is the fatal drying-up of the victuals avoided? To begin with, there are, so it seems to me, certain gifts bestowed on these little ones so inadequately protected by their mother's industry against the enemy, drought. I have seen Onthophagus- and Oniticellus-larvæ recover their appetite, their plumpness and their vigour under the wet cotton, after a three weeks' fast that had reduced them to a wrinkled pilule. This faculty of endurance has its uses: it enables the possessor to await, in a state of lethargy akin to death, the few, very uncertain drops of rain that will put an end to the famine. It comes to the grub's rescue, but it is not sufficient: the prosperity of a race cannot be based upon privation.

There is something more, therefore; and this is furnished by the mother's instinct. Whereas the manufacturers of pears and ovoids always dig their burrow at an open spot, with no other protection than the mound of earth flung up, the makers of little thimbles bore their well directly under the material exploited and go by preference to the voluminous droppings of the Horse and the Mule. Under this thick mattress, the soil, protected against sun and wind, keeps fresh and damp for some little time, steeped as it is in the moisture from the dung.

For that matter, the danger does not last long. The egg yields up the grub in less than a week; and the larva attains its full development within a dozen days or so, if nothing untoward happens. This makes about twenty days in all for the critical period of the Onthophagus and the Oniticellus. What does it matter if the walls of the emptied thimble do dry after that! The nymph will be all the better off in a solid casket, which will easily crumble to bits later, when, with the first September rains, the insect effects its release.

In appearance and habits the grub resembles that which the Sacred Beetle and the others have introduced to us. It possesses the same aptitude for defending the cell against the dangerous intrusion of the dry air; the same zeal, the same nimbleness in cementing the least breach with the putty of the intestines; the same knapsack hunching the middle of the back.

The grub of the Oniticellus has the most remarkable hump of all. Would you care to have a quick and yet a faithful sketch of it? Draw a short, wrinkled sausage. About the middle of this sausage, on the side, graft an appendix. There you have the beast, in three almost equal parts. The lower portion is the abdomen; the upper, where you are at first inclined to look for the head, so clearly does it appear to be a continuation of the part below, is the hump, the inordinate, extravagant hump, bigger than caricaturist ever dared conceive in the wildest flights of his imagination. It occupies the place which by rights belongs to the chest and head. Then where are these? Thrust aside by the monstrous knapsack, they constitute a lateral appendage, a mere knob. The strange creature bends at right angles under the weight of its hump.

When nature goes in for the grotesque, she leaves us behind. Is grotesque the right word? I have seen representations of Monkeys adorned with preposterous noses which Rabelais, for all his inspired vision of the huge, never conceived; and this though he invented the nose 'like the beak of a limbeck, in every part thereof most variously diapered with the twinkling sparkles of crimson blisters budding forth, and purpled with pimples all enamelled with thick-set wheals of a sanguine colour, bordered with gules.'3 I know some who are all scrubby with shock-headed wigs and whiskers and imperials in which every hairy drollery seems to be epitomized; and yet there is not a doubt that noses 'like the beak of a limbeck' and bristly faces are highly admired in the simian clan. There is no boundary between the fashionable and the grotesque. It all depends upon the appraiser.

If the grub with the outrageous hump were to show itself in public, it would doubtless represent the supreme expression of the beautiful in the eyes of the Oniticellus and the Onthophagus. Because it is a recluse, nobody sees it. Its charms would remain unknown but for the philosophical observer, who says to himself:

'Everything is good that harmonizes with the functions to be fulfilled. The grub requires a cement-bag to safeguard its provisions against desiccation; it is born with a knapsack on its back so that it may live.'

Thus is the hump excused and abundantly justified.

Its usefulness is displayed from another point of view. The thimble is of such a niggardly size that the grub consumes it almost entirely. All that remains is a thin layer, a crumbling remnant which would provide no security for the nymph. The ruined dwelling has to be strengthened, to be lined with a new wall. For this purpose, the larva of the Oniticellus empties the whole of its knapsack and gives its cell a complete coating of cement, after the manner of the Sacred Beetle and others.

The grub of the different species of Onthophagi does more artistic work. Placing its putty drop by drop, it constructs a mosaic of lightly-projecting scales, suggesting those of a cedar-cone. When finished, well dried and stripped of the last shreds of the original thimble, the shell thus obtained by the Bull Onthophagus is the size of an average filbert and resembles the pretty cone of the alder-tree. The imitation is so good that I was taken in by it the first time that I handled the curious product when digging in my cages. It needed the contents of the mock alder-cone to show me my mistake. The hump has an artfulness of its own: it was keeping this elegant specimen of stercoral jewellery in reserve for us.

The nymph of the Onthophagi provides us with another surprise. My observations are confined to two species only: the Bull Onthophagus and the Forked Onthophagus; but the difference between the two, in size and shape, is great enough to allow me to generalize and apply the following singular fact to the whole genus.

About the middle of the fore-edge of the corselet the nymph is armed with a very distinct horn, projecting for about one-twelfth of an inch. The horn is transparent, colourless and limp, as are all the budding organs at this period, particularly the legs, the cornicles of the forehead and the mouth-parts. This crystalline protuberance proclaims a future horn as clearly as the mandible is proclaimed by its initial nipple or the wing-case by its sheath. Any insect-collector will understand my amazement. A horn there, on the prothorax! But no Onthophagus wears such a weapon as that! The register of my insect-house duly records the genus of the insect, but I dare not believe it.

The nymph moults. Together with the cast skin, the unfamiliar horn dries up and falls off, leaving not the least trace behind it. My two Onthophagi, recently disguised in strange armour, now have their corselets bare.

This fleeting organ, which disappears without leaving even an excrescence, this temporary horn at a spot destined in the end to be unmailed, gives rise to a few reflections. The Dung-beetles, those placid creatures, generally favour a warlike harness: they love outlandish weapons, halberds, spears, grappling-irons, scimitars. Let us hurriedly recall the horn of the Spanish Copris. No Rhinoceros in the Indian jungles boasts one to compare with it upon his nose. Broad at the base, pointed at the tip, curved like a bow, when the head is lifted the horn bends back till it touches the keel of the obliquely truncated corselet. It might be a harpoon intended for ripping up some monster. Remember also the Minotaur,4 who looks as though he were going to spit his foe with his sheaf of three couched lances, and the Lunary Copris, horned on the forehead, armed with a pike on each shoulder and wearing a corselet notched with little crescents that remind us of the short curved knife of the pork-butcher.

The Onthophagi have a most varied arsenal. One, *O. taurus*, wears the Bull's crescent-shaped horns; a second, *O. vacca*, prefers a wide, short blade, with its point sheathed in a notch in the corselet; a third, *O. furcatus*, wields a trident; yet another, *O. nuchicornis*, owns a dagger with a winged handle; and again *O. cænobita* sports a cavalryman's sword. The worst-equipped crown their foreheads with a transversal crest, with a pair of cornicles.

What is the good of this panoply? Are we to look upon it as a set of tools, pickaxes, mattocks, pitchforks, spades, levers, which the insect might ply in digging? By no means. The only industrial implements are the forehead and the legs, especially the fore-legs. I have never discovered a Dung-beetle of any sort making use of her weapons either to excavate her burrow or to mix her provisions. Besides, as a rule, the direction of the things alone would prevent their employment as utensils. For a digging-job performed forwards, what would you have a Spanish Copris do with her pickaxe, which points backwards? The powerful horn does not face the obstacle attacked; it turns its back upon it.

The Minotaur's trident, though arranged in a suitable direction, likewise remains unemployed. When deprived of this armour with a clip of my scissors, the Beetle loses none of his mining-talents; he goes underground quite as easily as his unmutilated fellow. And here is an even more conclusive argument: the mothers, to whose lot the labour of nest-building falls; the mothers, those conspicuous workers, are deprived of these horny growths or possess them only on a greatly reduced scale. They simplify the armour, or reject it entirely, because it is more of an impediment than an assistance to their work.

Are we to look upon them as means of defence? Not that either. The ruminants, the main feeders of the dung-eaters, are also given to wearing frontal armour. The analogy of taste is obvious, though it is impossible for us to suspect its remote reasons. The Ram, the Bull, the Goat, the Chamois, the Stag, the Reindeer and the rest of them are armed with horns and antlers which they use in amorous jousts or for the protection of the threatened herd. The Onthophagi know nothing of these contests. There is no strife among them; and, should danger arise, they content themselves with shamming death by gathering their legs under their abdomen.

Their armour then is a mere ornament, the fine feathers of masculine coquetry. According to life's law of competition, the best-dressed carry off the palm. Though we may regard those rapiers on the nose as queer, their wearers are of another opinion; and the most eccentric enjoy the highest favour. The smallest extra pimple, springing up by accident, is an added beauty which may decide the choice among the suitors. The best-adorned captivate the mothers, perpetuate the breed and hand down to their offspring the cornicle or the knob that caused their triumph. Thus by degrees was the ornamentation at which the entomologist wonders to-day formed and transmitted from generation to generation, improving as it went.

To this *dictum* of the evolutionists the nymph of the Onthophagus replies as follows:

'I have on my back a budding horn, the germ of a bit of ornamentation that can be very handsome, as witness the Bison Bubas, who turns it into a splendid prow-shaped protuberance; witness also various exotic relatives of mine, who lengthen their corselet into a magnificent spur. I possess the wherewithal to bring about a revolution among my kin. If I retained it, my bump, that charming innovation, would relegate my rivals to the second rank; I should be preferred above all others; I should become the founder of a family; and my descendants, completing and improving on my first attempt, would behold the extinction of those antiquated old things. Why should the lump on my back wither purposeless? Why should my endeavour, repeated year after year for centuries, never achieve the promised result?'

Listen to me, O ambitious one! The theorists, it is true, declare that every casual acquisition, however trifling, is handed down and increases if it be profitable; but don't rely overmuch on that assertion. I do not doubt the advantages which you might gain from a little ornament. What I do very much doubt is the efficacity of time and environment as an evolutionary factor. You will be well-advised to believe that, born in the dim and distant past with a transient callosity, you are continuing and will continue to be born with that rudimentary excrescence without any chance of fixing it, hardening it into a horn or obtaining an additional decoration for your wedding-garment.

Be we men or Dung-beetles, we are all created in the image of an unalterable prototype: the changing conditions of life alter us slightly on the surface but never in the framework of our being. The verdigris of the ages may encrust our medals, but it can give them neither a new image nor a new superscription. Nothing will give me the wings of a bird, desirable though these would be in the midst of our human squalor; nor will anything bestow upon your adult age the triumphal crest which your nymphal knob seemed to prognosticate.

The nymphs of both the Onthophagus and the Oniticellus attain their maturity in some twenty days. During August the adult form appears with the half-white, half-red costume which has become familiar to us from our earlier studies. The normal colouring is fixed pretty quickly. Nevertheless the insect is in no hurry to burst its shell: the difficulty would be too great. It waits for the first showers of September, which will come to its assistance by softening the casket. The liberating rain arrives; and behold, issuing from the earth to rush after food, the joyous small fry of the Onthophagi.

Among the domestic secrets which my cages reveal to me at this period, one above all attracts my attention. I possess at the same time, in separate establishments, the newcomers and the veterans, which last are as brisk and eager in their pursuit of the victuals as are their sons, now banqueting for the first time in the open. The cages are stocked with two generations.

The same synchronizing of fathers and sons is observable among all the Dung-beetles that build their nests in the spring: Sacred Beetles, Copres and Geotrupes. The precaution which I have taken to watch the hatchings and to place the youngsters in a special compartment as and when they appeared confirms this remarkable simultaneity.

It is an entomological principle that the ancestor shall not see his descendants; he dies once the future of his family is assured. By a glorious privilege, the Sacred Beetle and his rivals are allowed to know their successors: fathers and sons meet at the same banquet, not in my cages, where the problems under consideration compel me to keep them separate, but in the open fields. Together they gambol in the sun, together they exploit the patch of dung encountered; and this life of revelry lasts as long as autumn continues to supply fine days.

The cold weather arrives. Sacred Beetles and Copres, Onthophagi and Gymnopleuri dig themselves a burrow, go down into it with provisions, shut themselves in and wait. In January, on a frosty day, I dig into the cages, which have no protection against the inclemencies of the season. I go to work discreetly, so as not to submit all my captives to the harsh test.

Those whom I exhume each sit huddled in a shell, beside the remaining provisions. All that the lethargy produced by the cold allows them to do is to move their legs and antennæ a little when I expose them to the sun.

Hardly has the imprudent almond-tree burst into blossom in February, when some of the sleepers awake. Two of the earlier Onthophagi, *O. lemur* and *O. fronticornis*, are very common at this time, already crumbling the dung warmed by the sun on the high-road. Soon the festival of spring begins; and all, large and small, newcomers and veterans, hasten to take part in it. The old ones, not all, but at least some of them, the best-preserved, fly off and get married a second time, an unparalleled privilege. They have two families, separated by an interval of a year. They can indeed have three, as is evidenced by the Broad-necked Scarab, who, kept in a cage for three years, gives me every year her collection of pears. Perhaps they even go beyond this. The Dung-beetle tribe has its patriarchs who are truly venerable.

1 ·546 × ·273 inch.—*Translator's Note.*

2 ·585 × ·39 inch.—*Translator's Note.*

3 *Pantagruel*: chap. i.; Sir Thomas Urquhart's translation.—*Translator's Note.*

4 *Minotaurus typhœus.* Cf. *The Life and Love of the Insect*: chap. x.—*Translator's Note.*

CHAPTER XII
THE GEOTRUPES: THE PUBLIC HEALTH

To complete the cycle of the year in the adult form, to see one's self surrounded by one's sons at the spring festival, to double and treble one's family: that surely is a most exceptional privilege in the insect world. The Bees, the aristocracy of instinct, perish once the honey-pot is filled; the Butterflies, the aristocracy not of instinct but of dress, die when they have fastened their packet of eggs in a propitious spot; the richly-armoured Ground-beetles succumb when the germs of a posterity are scattered beneath the stones.

So with the others, except among the social insects, where the mother survives, either alone or accompanied by her attendants. It is a general law: the insect is born orphaned of both its parents. And lo, by an unexpected turn of fate, the humble scavenger escapes the catastrophes that devour the mighty! The Dung-beetle, sated with days, becomes a patriarch.

This longevity explains first of all a fact that struck me long ago, when, to learn a little about the tribes whose history attracted me so greatly, I used to stick rows of Beetles on pins in my boxes. Ground-beetles, Rose-chafers, Buprestes, Capricorns, Saperdæ1 and the rest were collected one by one, after prolonged search. Now and again a lucky find would make my cheeks glow with excitement. Exclamations broke from our prentice band when one of these rarities was captured. A touch of jealousy accompanied our congratulations of the proud possessor. It was bound to be so; for think: there were not enough to go round.

A Scalary Saperda, the denizen of dead cherry-trees, clad in deep yellow with ladder-like markings of black velvet; a purply Ground-beetle, edged with amethyst along his ebony wing-cases; a brilliant Buprestis, wedding the sheen of gold and copper to the gorgeous green of malachite: these were great events, far too infrequent to satisfy us all.

With the Dung-beetles you can sing a different song! These are the ones if you want to fill the greediest of asphyxiating-phials to the neck. They, especially the smaller ones, are a numberless multitude when the others are few and far between. I remember Onthophagi and Aphodii swarming by the thousand under one shelter. You could have shovelled them up if you wished.

To this day I am still astonished when I see these crowds again; as of old, the abundance of the Dung-beetle family forms a striking contrast with the comparative scarcity of the others. If it occurred to me to go a-hunting once more and renew the quest to which I owe moments of such sheer delight, I should be certain of filling my flasks with Scarabæi, Copres, Geotrupes, Onthophagi and other members of the same corporation before achieving any measure of success with the rest of the series. By the time that May comes, the distiller of ordure is there in numbers; and in July and August, those months of blazing heat which see the suspension of labour in the fields, the dealer in unsavoury matter is still at work while the others have taken to earth and are lying in motionless torpor. He and his contemporary, the Cicada,2 represent almost by themselves such activity as prevails during the torrid days.

May not this greater frequency of the Dung-beetles, at least in my part of the world, be due to the longevity of the adult form? I think so. Whereas the other insects are summoned to enjoy the fine weather only in successive generations, these receive a general invitation, father and sons together, daughters and mother together. Being equally prolific, they are therefore represented twice over.

And they really deserve it, in consideration of the services which they render. There is a general hygienic law which requires that every putrid thing shall disappear in the shortest possible time. Paris has not yet solved the formidable problem of her sewage, which sooner or later will become a question of life or death for the monstrous city. One asks one's self whether the centre of light is not doomed to be extinguished some day in the reeking exhalations of a soil saturated with putrescence. What this agglomeration of millions of men cannot obtain, with all its treasures of wealth and talent, the smallest hamlet possesses without going to any expense or even troubling to think about it.

Nature, so lavish of her cares in respect of rural health, is indifferent to the welfare of cities, if not actively hostile to it. She has created for the fields two classes of scavengers, whom nothing wearies, whom nothing repels. One of these, consisting of Flies, Silphæ, Dermestes, Necrophori, Histers is charged with the dissection of corpses. They cut and hash, they elaborate the waste matter of death in their stomachs in order to restore it to life.

A Mole ripped open by the ploughshare soils the path with its entrails, which soon turn purple; a Snake lies on the grass, crushed by the foot of a wayfarer who thought, the fool, that he was performing a good work; an unfledged bird, fallen from its nest, lies, a crushed and pathetic heap, at the foot of the tree that carried it; thousands of other similar remains, of every sort and kind, are scattered here and there, threatening danger through their effluvia, if no steps be taken to put things right. Have no fear: no sooner is a corpse signalled in any direction than the little undertakers come trotting along. They work away at it, empty it, consume it to the bone, or at least reduce it to the dryness of a mummy. In less than twenty-four hours, Mole, Snake, bird have disappeared and the requirements of health are satisfied.

The same zeal for their task exists in the second class of scavengers. The village hardly knows those ammonia-scented refuges to which the townsman repairs to relieve his sordid needs. A little bit of a wall, a hedge, a bush is all that the peasant asks as a retreat at the moment when he would fain be alone. I need say no more to suggest the encounters to which such free and easy manners expose you! Enticed by the patches of lichen, the cushions of moss, the tufts of houseleek and other pretty things that adorn old stones, you go up to a sort of wall that supports a vineyard. Faugh! At the foot of the daintily-decked shelter, what an unconcealed abomination! You flee: lichens, mosses and houseleek tempt you no more. But come back on the morrow. The thing has disappeared, the place is clean: the Dung-beetles have been that way.

To preserve the eyes from a frequent recurrence of offensive sights is, to these stalwart workers, the least of their tasks: a loftier mission is incumbent on them. Science tells us that the most dreadful scourges of mankind have their agents of dissemination in tiny organisms, the microbes, near neighbours of must and mould, on the extreme confines of the vegetable kingdom. At times of epidemic, the terrible germs multiply by countless myriads in the intestinal discharges. They contaminate those main necessities of life, the air and the water; they spread over our linen, our clothes, our food and thus diffuse contagion. We have to destroy by fire, to sterilize with corrosives or to bury underground such things as are infected with them.

Prudence even demands that we should never allow ordure to linger on the surface of the ground. It may be harmless or it may be dangerous: when in doubt, the best thing is to put it out of sight. That is how ancient wisdom seems to have understood the thing, long before the microbe explained to us the need for vigilance. The nations of the east, more liable than we to epidemics, had formal laws in these matters. Moses, apparently echoing Egyptian knowledge in this case, tabulated the rules of conduct for his people wandering in the Arabian desert:

> 'Thou shalt have a place without the camp,' he says, 'to which thou mayst go for the necessities of nature, carrying a paddle at thy girdle. And, when thou sittest

> down, thou shalt dig round about and with the earth that is dug up thou shalt cover that which thou art eased of' (Deut. xxiii. 12–14).

The simple precept touches a matter of grave concern; and we may well believe that, if Islam, at the time of its great pilgrimages to the Kaaba, were to take the same precaution and a few more of a similar character, Mecca would cease to be an annual seat of cholera and Europe would not need to mount guard on the shores of the Red Sea to protect herself against the scourge.

Heedless of hygiene as the Arab, who was one of his ancestors, the Provençal peasant does not suspect the danger. Fortunately, the Dung-beetle, that faithful observer of the Mosaic law, is at work. It is his to remove from sight, it is his to bury the microbe-laden matter. Supplied with digging-implements far superior to the paddle which the Israelite was to carry at his girdle when urgent business called him from the camp, he hastens to the spot and, as soon as man is gone, excavates a pit wherein the infection is swallowed up and rendered harmless.

The services rendered by these sextons are of the highest importance to the health of the fields; yet we, who are those most interested in this constant work of purification, hardly vouchsafe the sturdy toilers a contemptuous glance. Popular language overwhelms them with harsh epithets. This appears to be the rule: do good and you shall be misjudged, you shall be traduced, stoned, trodden underfoot, as witness the Toad, the Bat, the Hedgehog, the Owl and other helpers who, for their services, ask nothing but a little tolerance.

Now, of our defenders against the dangers of filth flaunted shamelessly in the rays of the sun, the most remarkable in our climes are the Geotrupes: not that they are more zealous than the others, but because their size makes them capable of heavier work. Moreover, when it is simply a question of their nourishment, they resort by preference to the materials which we have most to fear.

My neighbourhood is worked by four species of Geotrupes. Two of them, *G. mutator*, Marsh, and *G. sylvaticus*, Panz., are rarities on which we had best not count for connected studies; the two others, on the contrary, *G. stercorarius*, Lin., and *G. hypocrita*, Schneid., are exceedingly common. Black as ink above, both of them are magnificently garbed below. We are quite surprised to find such a jewel-case among the professional scavengers. The under surface of the Stercoraceous Geotrupes is of a splendid amethyst-violet, while that of the Mimic Geotrupes makes a generous display of the ruddy gleams of copper pyrites. These two species are the inmates of my insect-houses.

Let us ask them first of what feats they are capable as buriers. There are a dozen of them in all. The cage is previously swept clean of what remains of the former provisions, hitherto supplied without stint. This time, I propose to find out what a Geotrupes can stow away in one night. At sunset, I serve to my twelve captives the whole of a heap which a Mule has just dropped in front of my door. There is plenty of it, enough to fill a basket.

On the morning of the next day, the mass has disappeared underground. There is nothing left outside, or very nearly nothing. I am able to make a fairly close estimate and I find that each of my Geotrupes, presuming each of the twelve to have done an equal share of the work, has buried pretty nearly sixty cubic inches of matter: a Titanic task, when we remember the insignificant size of the insect, which, moreover, has to dig the warehouse to which the booty must be lowered. And all this is done in the space of a night.

Having feathered their nests so well, will they remain quietly underground with their treasure? Not they! The weather is magnificent. The hour of twilight comes, gentle and calm. Now is the time when long flights are undertaken, when joyous humming fills the air, when the insects go afar, searching the roads by which the herds have lately passed. My lodgers abandon their cellars and mount to the surface. I hear them buzzing, climbing up the wirework, bumping wildly against the walls. I have anticipated this twilight animation. Provisions have been collected during the day, plentiful as those of yesterday. I serve them. There is the same disappearance during the night. On the morrow, the place is once again swept clean. And this would continue indefinitely, so fine are the evenings, if I always had at my disposal the wherewithal to satisfy these insatiable hoarders.

Rich though his booty be, the Geotrupes leaves it at sunset to dally in the last gleams of daylight and to go in search of a new workplace. With him, one would say, the wealth acquired does not count; the only thing of value is that to be acquired. Then what does he do with his warehouses, renewed each twilight in favourable weather? It is obvious that the Dung-beetle is incapable of consuming all those provisions in a single night. He has such a superabundance of victuals in his larder that he does not know how to dispose of them; he is surfeited with good things by which he will not profit; and, not satisfied with having his store crammed, the acquisitive plutocrat slaves, night after night, to store away more.

From each warehouse, set up here, set up there, as things happen, he deducts the daily meal beforehand; the rest, which means almost the whole, he abandons. My cages testify to the fact that this instinct for burying is more imperative than the consumer's appetite. The ground is soon raised, in consequence; and I am obliged, from time to time, to lower the level to the desired limits. If I dig it up, I find it choked throughout its depth with hoards that have remained intact. The original earth has become a hopeless conglomeration, which I must prune freely, if I would not go astray in my future observations.

Allowing for errors, either of excess or deficiency, which are inevitable in a subject that does not admit of exact measurement, one point stands out very clearly as the result of my enquiry: the Geotrupes are enthusiastic buriers; they take underground a great deal more than is necessary for their consumption. As this work is performed, in varying degrees, by legions of collaborators, large and small, it is evident that the purification of the soil must benefit to a considerable extent and that the public health is to be congratulated on having this army of auxiliaries in its service.

In addition, the plant and, indirectly, a host of different existences are interested in these interments. What the Geotrupes buries and abandons the next day is not lost: far from it. Nothing is lost in the world's balance-sheet; at stock-taking, the total never varies. The little lump of dung buried by the insect will make the nearest tuft of grass grow a luxuriant green. A Sheep passes, crops the bunch of grass: all the better for the leg of mutton which man is waiting for; the Dung-beetle's industry has procured us a savoury mouthful.

Even that is something, though we are making our usual mistake of comparing everything with our own standard. How much more it becomes, once we begin to think and get away from this narrow point of view! To enumerate all those who benefit, directly or indirectly, by the Dung-beetle's work would be impossible, so inextricably interlinked is all that exists. I think of the Warbler, who will stuff the mattress of his nest with the tiny stalks retted by the rain and sun; the caterpillar of some Psyche, which will construct its Moth-case by imbricating the remnants of those same stalks; little Cockchafers, who will nibble the anthers of the tall grasses; tiny Weevils, who will turn the ripe seeds into cradles for their grubs; tribes of Aphides, who will settle under the leaves; and Ants, who will come and slake their thirst at the sugary cornicles of the last-named herd.

Let us be content with this list, or we shall never have done. A whole world is benefited by the agricultural industry of the Dung-beetle, that burier of manure: first the plant and then all that live upon the plant. A small world, a very small world, as small as you please, but after all not a negligible world. It is of such trifles that the great integral of life is composed, even as the integral of the mathematicians is composed of quantities neighbouring on 0.

Agricultural chemistry teaches us that, to employ the stable-dung to the best purpose, we should put it into the ground, so far as possible, while fresh. When diluted by the rain and dissipated by the air, it becomes lifeless and devoid of fertilizing elements. This highly important agronomic truth is quite familiar to the Geotrupes and his colleagues. In their burying-work they invariably aim at materials of recent date. Just as they are eager to put away the produce of the moment, all saturated with its potassium, its nitrates and its phosphates, even so do they scorn the stuff hardened into brick by the sun or rendered infertile by long exposure to the air. The valueless residue does not interest them; they leave this barren rubbish to others.

We now know about the Geotrupes as a sanitary expert and a collector of manure. We are going to see him in a third aspect, that of the sagacious weather-prophet. It is popularly believed, in the country-side, that a swarm of agitated Geotrupes, skimming the ground with an air of great business in the evening, is a sign of fine weather on the morrow. Is this rustic prognostication worth anything? My cages shall tell us. I watch my boarders closely all through the autumn, the period when they build their nests; I note the state of the sky on the day before and register the weather of the next day. I use no thermometer, no barometer, none of the scientific implements employed in the meteorological observatories. I confine myself to the summary information derived from my personal impressions.

The Geotrupes do not leave their burrows until after sundown. With the last glimmer of daylight, if the air be calm and the temperature mild, they roam about, flying low with a humming noise, seeking the materials which have accumulated for them in the course of the day. If they come upon something that suits them, they drop down heavily, tumbling over in their clumsy eagerness, thrust themselves into their new treasure and spend the best part of the night in burying it. In this way the dirt of the fields is made to disappear in a single night.

There is one condition indispensable to this purging-process: the atmosphere must be still and warm. Should it rain, the Geotrupes will not stir out of doors. They have sufficient resources underground for a prolonged holiday. Should it be cold, should the north-wind blow, they will not sally forth either. In both cases my cages remain deserted on the surface. We will leave out of the question these periods of enforced leisure and consider only those evenings on which the atmospheric conditions are favourable to foraging-expeditions, or at least seem to me as though they ought to be. I will summarize the details in my note-book in three general cases.

First case. A glorious evening. The Geotrupes fuss about the cages, impatient to hasten to their nocturnal task. Next day, magnificent weather. The prophecy, of course, is of the simplest. To-day's fine weather is only the continuation of yesterday's. If the Geotrupes know nothing more than this, they hardly deserve their reputation. However, let us pursue the experiment before drawing any conclusions.

Second case. Again a fine evening. My experience seems to say that the condition of the sky forebodes a fine morning. The Geotrupes think otherwise. They do not come out. Which of the two will be right, man or Dung-beetle? The Dung-beetle: thanks to the keenness of his perceptions, he foresees, he scents a downpour. Rain comes during the night and lasts for part of the day.

Third case. The sky is overcast. Will the south-wind, gathering its clouds, bring us rain? I am of that opinion, appearances seem so much to point that way. The Geotrupes, however, fly and buzz around their cages. Their prophecy is correct and I am wrong. The threat of rain is dispelled and the sun next morning rises radiantly.

They seem to be influenced above all by the electric tension of the atmosphere. On hot and sultry evenings, when a storm is brewing, I see them moving about even more than usual. The morrow is always marked by violent claps of thunder.

There you have the upshot of my observations, which were continued for three months. Whatever the condition of the sky, whether clear or clouded, the Geotrupes announce fair weather or storm by their excited movements in the evening twilight. They are living barometers, more worthy of belief perhaps, in such contingencies, than the barometer of our scientists. The exquisite sensitiveness of life is mightier than the brute weight of a column of mercury.

I will end by mentioning a fact that well deserves further investigation when circumstances permit. On the twelfth, thirteenth and fourteenth of November 1894, the Geotrupes in my cages are in an extraordinarily agitated condition. Never before and never since have I seen such animation. They clamber wildly up the wires; at every moment they take wing and at once bump against the walls and are flung to the ground. Their restlessness continues until a late hour of the night, a very unusual thing with them. Out of doors, a few free neighbours run up and complete the riot in front of my house. What can be happening to bring these strangers here and especially to throw my cages into such a state of excitement?

After a few hot days, which are most exceptional at this time of the year, the south-wind prevails, foretelling that rain is at hand. On the evening of the fourteenth, an endless procession of broken clouds passes before the face of the moon. It is a magnificent sight. During the night the wind drops. There is not a breath of air. The sky is a uniform grey. The rain pours straight down, monotonously, continuously, depressingly. It looks as though it would never stop. And it goes on, in fact, until the eighteenth of the month.

Did the Geotrupes, who were so restless on the twelfth, foresee this deluge? They did. But as a rule they do not quit their burrows at the approach of rain. Something very extraordinary must have happened, therefore, to upset them in this way.

The newspapers explained the riddle. On the twelfth a storm of unprecedented violence burst over the north of France. The great barometrical depression which caused it was echoed in my district; and the Geotrupes marked this profound disturbance by their exceptional display of emotion. They told me of the hurricane before the papers did, had I but been able to understand them. Was this simply a chance coincidence, or was it a case of cause and effect? In the absence of sufficient evidence, I will end on this note of interrogation.

1 A genus of Longicorns, or Long-horned Beetles.—*Translator's Note.*

2 Cf. *The Life of the Grasshopper,* by J. Henri Fabre, translated by Alexander Teixeira de Mattos: chaps, i. to v.—*Translator's Note.*

CHAPTER XIII
THE GEOTRUPES: NEST-BUILDING

In September and October, when the first autumn rains soak the ground and allow the Sacred Beetle to split his natal casket, the Stercoraceous Geotrupes and the Mimic Geotrupes found their family-establishments: somewhat makeshift establishments, in spite of what we might have expected from the name of these miners, so well styled earth-borers. When he has to dig himself a retreat that shall shelter him against the rigours of winter, the Geotrupes really deserves his name: none can compare with him for the depth of the pit or the perfection and rapidity of the work. In sandy ground, easily excavated, I have dug up some that were buried over a yard deep. Others carried their digging farther still, tiring both my patience and my implements. There you have the skilled well-sinker, the inimitable earth-borer. When the cold sets in, he will be able to descend to some stratum where the frost has lost its terrors.

The family-lodging is another matter. The propitious season is a short one; time would fail, if each individual grub had to be endowed with one of those mansions. Nothing could be more satisfactory than for the insect to devote the leisure which the approach of winter gives it to digging a hole of unlimited depth: this makes the retreat doubly safe; and for the moment its energies, which are not yet suspended, have no other outlet. But at laying-time these laborious undertakings are impossible. The hours pass swiftly. In four or five weeks a numerous family has to be housed and victualled, which puts the sinking of a deep pit that requires time and patience quite out of the question.

In any case, precautions will be taken against the dangers of the surface. Once its family is settled, the unprotected adult insect is obliged to establish its winter quarters at great depths, whence it will emerge in spring accompanied by its young ones, like the Sacred Beetle; but neither the egg nor the grub needs this costly refuge in the wet season, being well protected by the parents' industry.

The burrow dug by the Geotrupes for the benefit of her grub is hardly deeper than that of the Copris or the Sacred Beetle, notwithstanding the difference of the seasons. Eleven or twelve inches, roughly speaking, is the most that I find in the fields, where nothing occurs to restrict the depth.

My cages, with their limited thickness of soil, are less trustworthy in this respect, since the insect has no option but to use the layer of earth at its disposal. Many a time, however, I perceive that this layer is not fully traversed down to the floor of the box, thus furnishing a fresh proof of the slight depth needed.

In the open fields as in the confinement of my cages, the burrow is always dug under the heap of dung that is being exploited. No outward sign betrays its presence, concealed as it is beneath the voluminous droppings of the Mule. It is a cylindrical passage, the same width as the neck of a claret-bottle, straight and perpendicular in a homogeneous soil, bent and winding irregularly in rough ground where a root or stone may bar the way and necessitate an abrupt change of direction. In my cages, when the layer of earth is insufficient, the pit, at first vertical, bends at right angles on touching the wooden floor and is continued horizontally. There is no precise rule therefore in the boring. The accidents of the soil determine the shape.

At the end of the gallery again there is nothing to remind us of the spacious hall, the workshop where Copres, Scarabæi and Gymnopleuri fashion their artistic pears and ovoids, but a mere *cul-de-sac* of the same diameter as the nest. A veritable drill-hole, if we make allowances for the occasional knots and twists inevitable in boring through stuff that offers more resistance at some places than at others; a winding channel: that is what the Geotrupes' burrow is.

The contents of the crude dwelling take the form of a sort of sausage or pudding, which fills the lower part of the cylinder and fits it exactly. Its length is not far short of eight inches and its width about an inch and a half, when the thing belongs to the Stercoraceous Geotrupes. The dimensions are a little smaller in the work of the Mimic Geotrupes. In either case, the sausage is nearly always irregular in shape, now curved, now more or less dented. These imperfections of the surface are due to the accidents of a stony ground, which the insect does not always excavate according to the canons of its art, which favours the straight line and the perpendicular. The moulded material faithfully reproduces all the irregularities of its mould. The lower end is rounded off like the bottom of the burrow itself; the upper end is slightly concave, through being packed more closely in the middle.

The voluminous object is put together in layers rather suggestive, as regards curve and arrangement, of a pile of watch-glasses. Each of them obviously corresponds with a load of materials gathered in the heap above the burrow, carried down separately, placed in position on the previous layer and then vigorously trampled flat. The edges of the disk, which adapt themselves less well to this work of compression, remain at a higher level; and all this tends to form something like a concave lens. These same less-compressed edges give a sort of rind, which is soiled with earth owing to its contact with the walls of the tunnel. Altogether, the structure tells us the method of manufacture. The Geotrupes' sausage, like our own, is obtained by moulding in a cylinder. It results from layers introduced one after the other and duly compressed, especially in the middle, which is more easily accessible to the manipulator's legs. Direct observation will presently confirm these inferences and supplement them with details of considerable interest, which we should never suspect from simply examining the work.

Before continuing, let us note how well inspired the insect is in always boring its burrow under the heap whence the materials for the sausage are to be extracted. The number of loads successively carried down and pressed is considerable. Allowing a thickness of a sixth of an inch for each layer—a figure which is near enough—I see that some fifty journeys are needed. If the provisions had each time to be fetched from a distance, the Geotrupes would be unable to cope with her task, which would be too long and tiring. Her sort of work is incompatible with all that travelling, after the fashion of the Sacred Beetle's. She is wise to settle beneath the heap. She has only to climb up from her well to find under her feet, at her very door, enough to make her black-pudding, however large she may wish it to be.

This, it is true, presupposes a copiously supplied workyard. When toiling on behalf of her grub, the Geotrupes keeps a look-out for one of this kind and accepts no purveyors except the Horse and the Mule, never the Sheep, who is too niggardly. It is not a question here of the quality of the foodstuffs; it is a question of quantity. My cages, in fact, tell me that the Sheep would have the preference, if she were more generous. What she does not give normally I create artificially by piling sheaf upon sheaf. Beneath this extraordinary treasure, the like of which is never offered by the fields, my captives work with a zest that shows how well they appreciate the windfall. They enrich me with more sausages than I know what to do with. I arrange them in strata in great pots, so that, when winter comes, I may study the actions of the larva; I lodge them separately in glass tubes and test-tubes; I pack them in tins. The shelves of my study are crammed with them. My collection reminds me of an assortment of potted meats.

The unfamiliarity of the material involves no change in the structure. Because of its finer grain and greater plasticity, the surface is more regular and the inside more homogeneous; and that is all.

At the lower end of the sausage, which end is always rounded off, is the hatching-chamber, a circular cavity which could hold a fair-sized hazel-nut. The respiratory needs of the germ demand that the side-walls should be thin enough to allow the air to enter freely. Inside, I catch the gleam of a greenish, semifluid plaster, a simple exudation from the porous mass, as in the Copris' ovoids and the Sacred Beetle's pears.

In this round hollow lies the egg, without adhering in any way to the surrounding walls. It is a white, elongated ellipsoid and is of remarkable bulk in proportion to the insect. In the case of the Stercoraceous Geotrupes, it measures seven to eight millimetres in length by four at its widest point.1 The egg of the Mimic Geotrupes is a little smaller.

This little hollow contrived in the substance of the sausage, at the lower end, does not agree at all with what I have read about the Geotrupes' nest-building. Quoting an old German writer, Frisch,2 an author whom the poverty of my library does not allow me to consult, Mulsant,3 speaking of the Stercoraceous Geotrupes, says:

> 'At the bottom of her perpendicular gallery, the mother builds, usually with earth, a sort of nest, or egg-shaped shell, open at one side. On the inner wall of this shell she glues a whitish egg, the size of a grain of wheat.'

What can this shell be, usually made of earth and open at one side so that the grub may reach the column of provisions overhead? I am at an utter loss to know. Shell, especially made of earth, there is none, nor any opening. I see and see again, as often as I wish, a round cell, closed everywhere and built at the lower end of the food-cylinder, but nothing else, nothing that even vaguely resembles the structure described.

Which of the two is responsible for the imaginary construction? Can the German entomologist have sinned through superficial observation? Or did the Lyons entomologist misinterpret the older author? I lack the necessary documents to bring the mistake home to the right person. Is it not pathetic to see these masters, who are so punctilious about a joint of the palpi, so cantankerous about the first claim to some barbaric appellation, almost indifferent when they come to treat of habits and industry, which are the supreme expression of an insect's life? Nomenclators' entomology is making enormous strides: it overwhelms us, swamps us. The other, biologists' entomology, the only interesting branch of the science, the only one really worthy of our attention, is neglected to such an extent that the commonest species has no history or calls for serious revision of the little that has been written about it. Vain lamentations: things will go on in the same old way for a long time to come.

To return to the Geotrupes' sausage. Its shape is diametrically opposite to that which we have studied in the case of the Copris and the Sacred Beetle, who are sparing of material but very generous with their labour, taking great care to give their work the shape best suited to preserve it against dryness. With their ovoids and their spheres surmounted by a neck, they are able to keep the modest family-ration fresh. The Geotrupes knows nothing of these scientific methods. More primitive in her ways, she sees well-being only in overabundance. Provided that the gallery be crammed with food, she little cares how shapeless her pile may be.

Instead of avoiding dryness, she appears to go in search of it. Just look at the sausage. It is inordinately long and clumsily put together. There is no compact, impermeable rind; and there is an excessive amount of surface, touching the earth for the whole length of the cylinder. This is exactly what is needed to bring about quick desiccation; it is the converse of the problem of the smallest surface, solved by the Sacred Beetle and the others. Then what becomes of my views on the shape of those provisions, views so well founded, according to our logic? Can I have been taken in by a blind geometry, which achieves a rational result by chance?

To any one who says so let the facts reply. Here is their answer: the manufacturers of spheres build their nests at the height of the summer, when the ground is parched; the manufacturers of cylinders build theirs in the autumn, when the earth becomes saturated with rain. The first have to guard their family against the danger of bread too hard to eat. The second know nothing of starvation through desiccation; their provisions, potted in cool earth, retain indefinitely the proper degree of softness. The moistness, not the shape, of the sheath is the safeguard of the ration inside it. The rainfall at this time of the year is in inverse ratio to that of summer; and this is enough to render useless the precautions taken in the dog-days.

Let us probe deeper and we shall see that the cylinder is preferable to the sphere in autumn. When October and November come, the rains are frequent and persistent; but a day's sunshine is enough to dry the soil to the shallow depth where the Geotrupes' nest lies. It is a serious matter not to lose the enjoyment of this fine day. How will the grub benefit by it?

Imagine the larva enclosed in the big ball which the copious quantity of food placed at its disposal might well supply. Once saturated with moisture by a shower, this sphere would retain it stubbornly, for its form is that of least evaporation and of least contact with the sun-warmed soil. In vain, within twenty-four hours, will the surface layer of the ground be restored to its normal coolness: the globular mass will retain its excess of water, for lack of adequate contact with the sun- and air-dried earth. In the too-humid and too-thick recess, the provisions will go musty; the heat from outside will be inopportune, as will the air; and the larva will derive little advantage from this late autumn sun, whose tardy rays ought to ripen it to perfection and give it the necessary vigour to brave the trials of winter.

What was a good quality in July, when it was necessary to guard against excessive dryness, becomes a bad one in October, when excessive damp is to be avoided. The cylinder is therefore substituted for the sphere. The new shape, with its exaggerated length, fulfils the converse condition of that beloved by the pill-makers: here, with a similar volume, the surface is developed to its extreme limits. Is there a reason for this complete change? No doubt; and I seem to perceive it. Now that dryness is no longer to be feared, will not this kind of shape, with its large surface, enable the mass of foodstuff to get rid of its superfluous moisture more readily? Should it rain, its wide area certainly will make it liable to more rapid saturation; but also, when the fine weather returns, the surplus water will soon disappear thanks to the extensive contact with a quickly-drained soil.

Let us conclude by enquiring how the roly-poly is manufactured. To watch the performance in the fields appears to me a very difficult, not to say impracticable undertaking. With my cages, success is certain, provided that we exercise a little patience and dexterity. I let down the board which keeps the artificial soil in place at the back. This now reveals its vertical surface, which I explore bit by bit with the point of a knife until I strike a burrow. If the operation be cautiously conducted, without the disturbance due to an ill-calculated landslip, the labourers are discovered at their toil, paralysed, it is true, by the sudden flood of light and as it were petrified in the attitude of work. The arrangement of the workshop and the materials, the position and posture of the workers enable us easily to reconstruct the scene, though it be abruptly suspended and not renewed so long as our inspection lasts.

One fact, to begin with, thrusts itself upon our attention, a fact of deep interest and so exceptional that this is the first example with which my entomological studies have presented me. In each burrow laid bare I always find two collaborators, a pair: I find the male lending the mother his assistance. The household duties are divided between the two. My notes give the following scene, to which we can easily restore its animation according to the pose of the immobilized actors.

The male is at the back of the gallery, squatting on a length of sausage measuring barely an inch. He occupies the basin formed through the stuff's being packed more tightly in the centre of each stratum. What was he doing before the violation of his home? His attitude tells us clearly: with his sturdy legs, especially the hind-legs, he was pressing down the last layer placed in position. His mate occupies the upper floor, almost at the opening of the burrow. I see her holding between her legs a great lump of material which she has just gathered at the bottom of the heap surmounting the house. The scare caused by my intrusion has not made her let go. Hanging up there, above space, braced against the walls of the pit, she clasps her burden with a sort of cataleptic obstinacy. The nature of the interrupted work is easily guessed: Baucis was carrying down to Philemon, the stronger of the two, the wherewithal to continue the arduous work of piling and trampling. After laying the egg and surrounding it with those delicate precautions of which a mother alone possesses the secret, she had handed over the construction of the cylinder to her companion, confining herself to playing the humble part of a caterer's man.

Similar scenes, observed during different phases of the work, enable me to draw a general picture. The sausage begins with a short, wide casing which closely lines the bottom of the burrow. In this bag, with its yawning mouth, I find the two sexes in the midst of materials crumbled and possibly weeded before being pressed, so that the grub may have first-class victuals within its reach as soon as it starts feeding. The couple between them plaster the walls and increase their thickness until the cavity is reduced to the size needed for the hatching-chamber.

This is the moment for laying the egg. Withdrawing discreetly, the male waits with materials ready to close the cell that has just been filled. The closing is done by bringing the edges of the sack nearer together and adding a ceiling, a hermetically cemented lid. This is the delicate part of the work, calling for knack much more than strength. The mother alone attends to it. Philemon is now a mere journeyman-mason: he passes the mortar, without being allowed on the ceiling, which his brutal pressure might cause to fall in.

Soon the roof, duly thickened and reinforced, has nothing more to fear from pressure. Then the ruthless stamping begins, the rough work which transfers the leading part to the male. In the Stercoraceous Geotrupes the difference in size and vigour between the sexes is striking. Here indeed we have a very exceptional case: Philemon belongs to the stronger sex. He is distinguished by his portly figure and muscular energy. Take him in your hand and squeeze. I defy you to stand it, if your skin is at all sensitive to pain. With his sharp-toothed and convulsively stiffened legs, he digs into your flesh; he slips like an irresistible wedge into the spaces between your fingers. It is more than you can bear; and you have to let the creature go.

In the household he performs the function of an hydraulic press. We subject our packs of fodder to the action of the press in order to reduce their cumbrous bulk; he likewise compresses and reduces the stringy materials of his sausage. It is most often the male that I find at the top of the cylinder, a top excavated to form a deep basket. This basket receives the load brought down by the mother; and, like the labourer trampling on the grapes at the bottom of the vintage-tub, the Geotrupes presses and amalgamates his materials with the convulsive effort of his galvanic movements. The operation is so well conducted that the new load, at first not unlike a voluminous mass of coarse lint, becomes a compact layer uniform with the one before it.

The mother, however, does not abdicate her rights: I find her now and then at the bottom of the basin. Perhaps she has come to see how the work is going on. Her touch, which is better-suited for the delicate part of the rearing, will more readily discover the mistakes that need correcting. Very likely also she comes to relieve her husband in these exhausting compressive operations. She herself is strong, sturdy in the legs and capable of working turn and turn about with her valiant companion.

However, her usual place is at the top of the gallery. I find her there at one time with the armful which she has just gathered, at another with a heap made up of several loads placed in reserve for the work down below. As and when it is wanted, she draws upon the heap and gradually carries the materials down to be pressed by the male.

Between this temporary warehouse and the basin at the bottom there is a long empty space, the lower part of which supplies us with another bit of information as to the progress of the work. The walls are lavishly coated with a wash extracted from the most plastic portion of the materials. This detail is not without value. It tells us that, before packing the food-sausage layer by layer, the insect begins by cementing the rough and porous wall of the mould. It putties its well to protect the grub against the damp which might ooze through in the rainy season. Finding it impossible by pressure to harden the skin of the tightly-packed sausage to the requisite degree, it adopts a means unknown to the Beetles that labour in large workshops; it coats the earthy casing with cement. In this way it avoids, so far as lies in its power, the risk of drowning on rainy days.

This waterproofing is done at intervals, as the cylinder grows in length. The mother appears to me to attend to it whenever her warehouse of provisions is sufficiently stocked to give her the time. While her companion is pressing, she, an inch higher up, is plastering.

At last the combined efforts of husband and wife result in a cylinder of the regulation length. The greater part of the well above remains empty and uncemented. Nothing tells me that the Geotrupes trouble about this unoccupied area. Scarabæi and Copres shoot into the entrance-passage to the underground chamber a portion of the rubbish extracted; they build a barricade in front of the dwelling. The sausage-makers seem to be unfamiliar with this precaution. All the burrows which I inspect are empty in the upper part. There is no sign of excavated earth put back and pressed into position; there is merely a little fallen rubbish, coming either from the dung-heap above or from the crumbling walls.

This neglect might well be ascribed to the thick roof that surmounts the house. Remember that the Geotrupes generally settle under the copious provender which the Horse and the Mule bestow upon them. Under such a shelter, is it really necessary to bolt one's door? Besides, the rough weather looks after the closing for them. The roof falls in, the earth slips and the yawning pit soon fills up without the assistance of those who dug it.

Just now my pen ventured to write the names of Philemon and Baucis. As a matter of fact, the Geotrupes couple do in certain respects recall the peaceful mythological household. What is the male, in the insect world? Once the wedding has been celebrated, he is an incompetent, an idler, a good-for-nothing, a drug in the market whom others shun and sometimes even get rid of by atrocious means. The Praying Mantis4 tells us tragic enough things in this connection.

Now here, by a very curious exception, the sluggard becomes a toiler; the lover of the moment a faithful husband; the careless parent a serious *paterfamilias*. The brief meeting changes into a lasting partnership. Married life, domestic life comes into being: a glorious innovation; and the pioneer is a Dung-beetle! Go downwards: there is nothing resembling it; go upwards: for a long time there is still nothing. We have to mount to the top of the scale.

Take that little fish of our brooks, the Stickleback. The male knows very well how to build out of algæ and different water-weeds a nest, a snuggery, in which the female will come and spawn; but he knows nothing of work shared in common. The cares of a family in which the mother takes little interest fall upon him alone. No matter: there is one step gained, a great one and especially a very remarkable one among fishes, who are so supremely indifferent to family-affection and substitute an appalling fecundity for the trouble of breeding. Fabulous numbers make good the voids due to the lack of industry in the parents, even in the mother, a mere bag for eggs.

Certain Toads attempt the duties of paternity; and then we have nothing more till we come to the bird, that paragon of the domestic virtues. Here we find married life in all its moral beauty. A contract turns the couple into two collaborators, both equally zealous for the prosperity of the family. The father takes just as much part as the mother in the building of the nest, the quest of provisions, the distribution of each mouthful and the supervision of the youngsters as they try their wings preliminary to their first flight.

Standing still higher in the animal scale, the mammal carries on the wonderful example without adding to it; on the contrary, it often simplifies things. Man remains and has no prouder title to nobility than his unwearying care for the family, that alliance which is never dissolved. To our shame, I admit, a few individuals deny their responsibility and sink below the level of the Toad.

The Geotrupes rivals the bird. The nest is the joint production of husband and wife. The father puts the various layers together and compresses them; the mother plasters the walls, fetches fresh loads and places them under the presser's feet. This home, the outcome of the couple's efforts, is also a storehouse of provisions. Here we see no mouthfuls distributed to the children from day to day, but the food-problem is solved none the less: the united labours of the two partners result in the sumptuous sausage. Father and mother have done their duty splendidly; they bequeath to the grub an eminently well-furnished larder.

A pair that continue to exist as such, a couple that join forces and unite their industry for their offspring's welfare, certainly represent enormous progress, perhaps the greatest in the animal kingdom. One day, in the midst of the isolated existences, the household appeared, the invention of an inspired Dung-beetle. How is it that his magnificent acquirement is the property of a few, instead of extending all around, from one species to another, throughout the guild? Can it be that Scarabæi and Copres would have nothing to gain, in saving of time and labour, if the mother, instead of working alone, had an assistant? Things would move faster, so it seems to me, and a more numerous family would be permissible, a possibility not to be despised when one has an eye to the prosperity of the species.

How, on his side, did the Geotrupes think of combining the two sexes in building the nest and stocking the larder? The abrupt transformation of the usual airy paternity of the insect into something that rivals motherhood in tenderness is so serious and so rare an event that we long to discover the cause of it, if indeed we may hope to do so with the sorry means of information at our disposal. One idea occurs to us at once: may there not be some connection between the male's superior size and his liking for hard work? Endowed with greater robustness and vigour than the mother, he who is usually so lazy has become a zealous helper; the love of work has come from a surplus of unspent strength.

Take care: this apparent explanation will not hold water. The two sexes of the Mimic Geotrupes scarcely differ in size; the advantage is often even in the female's favour; and nevertheless the male lends assistance to his companion: he is as eager a well-sinker, as energetic a presser as his big stercoraceous kinsman.

And here is a still more conclusive argument: among the Anthidia,5 those Bees who weave cotton-stuffs or knead resin, the male, though much larger than the female, is an absolute idler. He, so strong, so stout of limb, take part in the work! Never! Let the mother, the feeble mother, wear herself out while he, powerful fellow that he is, frolics among the speedwell and the lavender.

It is not physical strength, therefore, that has made the Geotrupian *paterfamilias* into a worker devoted to his children's welfare. And this is as much as our investigations tell us. To pursue the problem would be a vain endeavour. The origin of faculties escapes us. Why is this gift bestowed here and that gift there? Who knows? Can we indeed ever hope to know?

One point alone stands out clearly: instinct is not dependent on structure.

The Geotrupes have been known from time immemorial; conscientious entomologists, peering through their magnifying-glasses, have examined them down to their smallest details; and no one has yet suspected their marvellous privilege of keeping house in common. Above the monotonous level of the ocean suddenly emerge the headlands of lonely little islands, scattered here and there, whose existence none can suspect until geography has added them to her charts. Even so do the peaks of instinct rear their crests above the ocean of life.

1 ·273 to ·312 × ·156 inch.—*Translator's Note.*

2 Johann Leonhard Frisch (1666–1743), a Lutheran clergyman, lexicologist and natural historian and member of the Berlin Academy. His *Beschreibung von allerlei Insecten in Deutschland* was published in 1720 to 1738.—*Translator's Note.*

3 Martial Étienne Mulsant (1797–1880), professor of natural history at the Lycée de Lyon; author of *Histoire naturelle des coléoptères de France* (1839–1846) and other entomological works.—*Translator's Note.*

4 Cf. *The Life of the Grasshopper*: chaps. vi. to ix.—*Translator's Note.*

5 Cf. *Bramble-bees and Others*: chaps. ix. and x.—*Translator's Note.*

CHAPTER XIV
THE GEOTRUPES: THE LARVA

The egg takes from one to two weeks to hatch, according as it is laid in October or September. As a rule the hatching takes place in the first fortnight of October. The larva grows pretty quickly and soon manifests very different characteristics from those displayed by the other Dung-beetles. We find ourselves in a new world, full of surprises. The grub is folded in two, it is bent into a hook, as required by the narrowness of the cell, which is scooped out gradually as the inside of the sausage is consumed.

Even so did the grubs of the Sacred Beetle, the Copris and the others comport themselves; but the larva of the Geotrupes has not the hump that gave the first-named such an ungainly figure. Its back is curved regularly. This entire absence of a knapsack, of a putty-bag, points to different habits. The larva, in fact, is not acquainted with the art of plugging crevices. If I contrive an opening in the part of the sausage which it occupies, I do not see it taking note of the hole, turning round and forthwith repairing the damage with a few pats of a trowel well supplied with cement. The access of the air does not trouble it apparently, or rather there is no provision against this in its means of defence.

You have only to take a glance at its dwelling. What would be the use of the plasterer's art of stopping up crannies, when the house simply cannot crack? Closely moulded in the cylinder of the burrow, the sausage is preserved from crumbling to dust by the support of its mould. The Sacred Beetle's pear, which is free on every side in a large underground cavity, often swells, splits, peels off. The Geotrupes' sausage, being packed in a casing, is free from these imperfections. Besides, if it were to burst, the accident would not be serious, for now, in autumn and winter, in a soil that is always damp and fresh, there is no fear of that desiccation which is so greatly dreaded by the pill-rollers. Hence there is no special industry designed to circumvent a peril that is unlikely and of little consequence; no excessively docile intestine to keep the trowel supplied; no ugly hump to act as a mortar-magazine. The inexhaustible evacuator of our earlier studies disappears and is replaced by a grub whose motions are more moderate.

Obviously, big eater as the larva is and, moreover, sequestered in a cell allowing of no communication with the outside, it is utterly ignorant of what we call cleanliness. Let us not take this to mean that it is disgustingly filthy, soiled with excrement: we should be making a grave mistake. Nothing could be neater or glossier than its satiny skin. We wonder what pains it must take over its toilet, or else what special grace enables all these eaters of ordure to keep themselves so clean. Seeing them outside their usual environment, no one would suspect their sordid life.

We must look elsewhere for any defect in cleanliness, if indeed it is right to give the name of defect to a quality which, all things considered, makes for the creature's good. Language, the one and only mirror of our thoughts, easily goes astray and becomes treacherous when attempting to express reality. Let us substitute the larva's point of view for our own, let us throw off the man and become the Dung-beetle: offensive epithets will disappear forthwith.

The grub, that mighty eater, has no relations with the outside world. What is it to do with the remains of what it has digested? Far from being embarrassed by them, it takes advantage of them, as do many other solitaries cabined in a shell. It uses them to keep out the draughts from its hermitage and to pad it with quilting. It spreads them into a soft couch, grateful to its delicate skin; it builds them into a polished niche, a water-tight alcove which will protect the long winter torpor. I told you that one had but to imagine one's self a Dung-beetle for a moment in order to change one's language utterly. Behold that which was hateful and burdensome turned into something of value, which will contribute largely to the grub's welfare. Onthophagi and Copres, Scarabæi and Gymnopleuri have accustomed us to this kind of industry.

The sausage is in an upright position, or nearly so. The hatching-chamber is at the bottom end. As the grub grows, it attacks the provisions overhead, but does not touch the wall around, which is of considerable thickness. It has indeed so huge a dish at its disposal that abstinence becomes no difficult matter. The Sacred Beetle's grub, which has no occasion to take precautions against the winter, has a very skimpy helping. Its little pear is a niggardly ration and is consumed throughout, all but a slender wall, which the inmate, however, takes care to thicken and strengthen with a good layer of its mortar. The grub of the Geotrupes is very differently situated. It is supplied with a colossal sausage, representing nearly a dozen times as much as the other provisions. However well endowed it be with stomach and appetite, it could not possibly consume the whole lot. Besides, the question of food is not the only one to be considered this time: there is also the serious matter of the hibernation. The parents foresaw the severity of the winter and bequeathed their sons the wherewithal to face it. The giant roly-poly will become a blanket against the cold.

The grub, as a matter of fact, gnaws bit by bit the part above and scoops out a corridor just wide enough to pass through. In this way, a very thick wall is left intact, the central part alone being consumed. As the sheath is bored, the sides are at the same time cemented and lined with the evacuations of the intestine. Any excess product accumulates and forms a rampart behind.

So long as the weather remains favourable, the grub moves about in its gallery; it takes its stand above or below and attacks the provisions with a tooth that grows daily more languid. Five or six weeks are thus passed in banqueting; then comes the cold weather, bringing the winter torpor with it. The grub now digs itself an oval recess, polished by much wriggling of its body, at the lower end of its case, in the mass of material which digestion has transformed into a fine paste; it protects itself with a curved canopy; and it is ready to enjoy its winter slumbers. It can sleep in peace. If its parents have installed it underground at an inconsiderable depth to which the frost penetrates, at any rate they have increased the supply of victuals to the utmost. The effect of this enormous superfluity is to provide an excellent dwelling for the bad weather.

In December the grub is full-grown, or not far short of it. If the temperature only lent a hand, the nymphosis would now be due. But times are hard; and the grub, in its wisdom, decides to defer the delicate work of transformation. Sturdy creature that it is, it will be able to resist the cold much better than the nymph, that frail beginning of a new life. It therefore has patience and tarries in a state of torpor. I take it from its cell to examine it.

Convex on top and almost flat below, the larva is a semicylinder bent into a hook. There is an entire absence of the hump belonging to the previous Dung-beetles; likewise of any terminal trowel. The plasterer's art of repairing crevices being unknown here, there is no need for the cement-pot or the spreading-utensil. The creature's skin is smooth and white, clouded in the hinder half by the dark contents of the intestines. Sparse hairs, some fairly long, others very short, stand up on the median and dorsal region of the segments. They apparently serve to help the grub move about its cell by the mere wriggling of its hinder part. The head is neither big nor small and is pale-yellow in colour; the mandibles are large and brown at the tip.

But let us leave these details, which are of no great interest, and say at once that the creature's prominent characteristic is supplied by its legs. The first two pairs are pretty long, especially for an animal leading a sedentary life in a narrow cabin. They are normally constructed; and it must be their strength that allows the grub to clamber about inside its pudding, converted into a sheath by eating. But the third pair presents a peculiarity of which I know no example elsewhere.

The limbs forming this pair are rudimentary legs, crippled from birth, impotent, arrested in their development. They give one the impression of lifeless stumps. Their length is hardly a third of that of the others. More remarkable still, instead of pointing downwards like the normal legs, they shrivel upwards, turning towards the back, and remain indefinitely in that queer attitude, twisted and stiff. I cannot succeed in seeing the animal make the slightest use of them. Nevertheless they show the same joints as the others; but this is all on a greatly reduced scale, pale and inert. In short, a couple of words will distinguish the Geotrupes' larva without any possibility of confusion: hind-legs atrophied.

This feature is so plain, so striking, so extraordinary that the least observant among us cannot mistake it. A grub crippled by nature and so evidently crippled enforces itself on our attention. What do the books say about it? Nothing, so far as I know. The few which I have with me are silent on this point. Mulsant, it is true, described the larva of the Stercoraceous Geotrupes; but he makes no mention of its exceptional structure. In his anxiety to describe the minutest details of the organism, has he lost sight of this monstrosity? Labrum, palpi, antennæ, the number of joints, the hairs: all this is set down and scrutinized; and the lifeless legs reduced to stumps are passed over in silence. Are the experts then so busy with the Gnat that they cannot see the Camel? I give it up.

Observe also that the hind-legs of the perfect insect are longer and stronger than the middle-legs and vie with the fore-legs in vigour. The atrophied limbs of the grub, therefore, become the adult's powerful pressing-machine; the impotent stumps change into strong stamping-tools.

Who will tell us the origin of these anomalies now thrice observed among the dung-workers? The Sacred Beetle, who is sound in every limb during his infancy, loses his fore-fingers when the adult form appears; the Onthophagus, who sports a horn on his thorax in his nymphal stage, drops it and does without the ornament in the end; the Geotrupes, at first a limping grub, turns his useless stumps into the best of his levers. The last-named makes progress; the others retrocede. Why does the cripple become able-bodied and why do the able-bodied become cripples?

We make chemical analyses of the suns; we surprise the nebulæ in labour and watch the birth of worlds; and shall we never know why a miserable grub is born limping? Come, ye divers who fathom life's mysteries, descend a little lower into the depths and at least bring us back that humble pearl, the reply to the problems of the Geotrupes and the Sacred Beetle!

When the weather is severe, what becomes of the larva in the retreat which it has succeeded in making at the far end of its box? The exceptional cold of January and February 1895 will answer this question. My cages, always left in the open air, had repeatedly undergone a drop in temperature of some ten degrees below freezing-point. In this arctic weather, I conceived a wish to go in search of information and learn how things were progressing in my unprotected cages.

I could not manage it. The bed of earth, wetted by the earlier rains, had become a compact block throughout, which I should have had to break up like a stone with a hammer and chisel. Extraction by violent means was not practicable: I should have endangered everything with my hammering. On the other hand, if any life remained in the frozen mass, I should have placed it in jeopardy by changing the temperature too suddenly. It was better to await the very slow natural thaw.

Early in March I inspect the cages again. This time there is no ice left. The earth is yielding and easy to dig. All the adult Geotrupes have died, bequeathing me a fresh supply of sausages, almost as plentiful as that which I had gathered and placed in safety in October. They have all perished; there is not a single survivor. Is cold or old age to blame?

At this very time and later, in April and May, when the new generation is wholly in the larval or at most in the nymphal stage, I often find adult Geotrupes busy in their scavenging-works. The old ones therefore see a second spring; they live long enough to know their children and to work with them, as do the Scarabæi, the Copres and others. These early ones are veterans. They have escaped the hardships of winter because they have been able to bury themselves far enough underground. Mine, kept captive between a few boards, have died for want of a sufficiently deep pit. At a time when they needed three feet of earth to shelter themselves, they had less than twelve inches. It was cold, therefore, that killed them, rather than age.

The low temperature, while fatal to the adult, has spared the larva. The few sausages left in position after my October diggings contain the grub in excellent condition. The protecting sheath has fulfilled its office to perfection: it has preserved the sons from the catastrophe that caused the death of the parents.

The other cylinders, fashioned in the course of November, contain something even more remarkable. In their hatching-chamber, at the bottom, they hold an egg, all plump and shiny and as healthy-looking as though it had been laid that day. Can life still exist there? Is it possible, after the best part of the winter has been passed in a block of ice? I dare not believe it. The sausage itself has not an attractive appearance. It is darkened by fermentation, smells musty and does not suggest food worth having.

At all events, I will take the precaution of bottling the miserable puddings, after ascertaining that the egg is there in each case. I was well-advised. The fresh aspect of the germs, after wintering under such rude conditions, did not belie them. The hatching was soon effected; and early in May the late arrivals were almost as well-developed as their seniors, hatched in the autumn.

Some interesting facts are revealed by this piece of observation. First of all, the laying-period of the Geotrupes is a fairly long one, lasting from September to some time in November. At that date the first hoar-frosts begin; the soil is not warm enough to hatch the eggs; and the last ones, unable to hatch as swiftly as their predecessors, wait for the return of the fine weather. A few mild April days are enough to reawaken their suspended vitality. Then the usual evolution goes on, and this so rapidly that, notwithstanding a delay of five or six months, the backward larvæ are very nearly as big as the others by May, when the first nymphs appear.

Secondly, the Geotrupes' eggs are capable of enduring the trials of severe cold unscathed. I do not know the exact temperature inside the frozen block which I tried to tackle with a mason's chisel. Outside, the thermometer sometimes fell to ten degrees below freezing-point; and, as the cold period lasted a long time, we may believe that the layer of earth in my boxes was equally cold. Now the Geotrupes' puddings were enclosed in that frozen mass turned to a block of stone. A generous allowance must no doubt be made for the non-conductivity of these puddings composed of thready materials; the wall of dung did, to a certain extent, protect the larva and the egg against the biting cold, which, if experienced direct, would have been fatal. No matter: in that atmosphere the dung-cylinders, damp at the start, must in the long run have acquired the hardness of stone. In their hatching-chamber, in the tunnel made by the larva, the temperature undoubtedly sank below freezing-point.

Then what became of the grub and the egg? Were they really frozen? Everything seems to tell us so. That this most delicate of all delicate things, a germ, a rudiment of life in a blob of glair, should harden, turn into a bit of stone and then resume its vitality and continue its evolution after thawing seems inadmissible. And yet circumstances confirm it. We should have to credit the Geotrupes' sausages with athermanous properties unequalled by any other substance to regard them as a sufficient protection against such intense and lasting refrigeration. What a pity that we could derive no information from the thermometer in this instance! After all, if complete freezing is unproven, one point has been established for certain: the egg and the grub of the Geotrupes can support and survive very low temperatures in their protecting sheath.

Since the occasion presents itself, let me say a few more words on the insect's powers of resisting cold. Some years ago, while looking for Scolia-cocoons in a heap of mould, I had made a large collection of the grubs of *Cetonia aurata*.1 I placed my loot in a flower-pot with a few handfuls of decayed vegetable matter, just enough to cover the insects' backs. I intended to draw upon them for certain enquiries which I was making at the time. The pot remained in the open air; and I forgot all about it. A cold snap came, accompanied by sharp frost and snow. Then I remembered my Cetoniæ, so ill-protected against this kind of weather. I found the contents of the pot hardened into a conglomeration of earth, dead leaves, ice, snow and shrivelled grubs. It was a sort of almond-rock, in which the larvæ stood for the almonds. Sorely tried by the cold as they were, the colony ought to have perished. But no: when the thaw arrived, the frozen larvæ came to life again and began to swarm about as though nothing unusual had happened.

The insect's powers of endurance are less great than the larva's. As the organization becomes more refined, it loses its robustness. My cages, which went through such a bad time in the winter of 1895, provided me with a striking instance. A few species—Scarabæi, Copres, Pilularii and Onthophagi—were represented at the same time by newcomers and old stagers. All the Geotrupes, without an exception, died in the earthy bed which had turned into a block of stone; the Minotaurs also succumbed, every one of them. And yet both find their way up north and are not afraid of cold climates. On the other hand, the southern species, the Sacred Beetle, the Spanish Copris and *Pilularius flagellatus*, the younger generation as well as the veterans, withstood the winter better than I dared hope. Many of them died, it is true; they formed the majority; but at any rate there were survivors whom I marvelled to see recovering from their icy paralysis, trotting about under the first kisses of the sun. In April, those specimens which have escaped from freezing resume their labours. They teach me that, when at liberty, Copres and Scarabæi have no need to retire to winter quarters at great depths underground. A moderate screen of earth, in some sheltered nook, is enough for them. Less skilful diggers than the Geotrupes, they are better provided with the power to resist a passing spell of cold.

We will end this digression by remarking, as so many others have done, that agriculture cannot reckon on the cold weather to rid it of its dread enemy, the insect. Very hard frosts, lasting a long time and penetrating well beneath the surface of the soil, can destroy various species which are not able to go down low enough; but a great many survive. Moreover, the grub and especially the egg in many cases defy our severest winters.

The first five days of April put an end to the torpor of the larvæ of both Geotrupes, snuggling on the bottom floor of their cylinder, in a temporary cell. Activity returns, bringing with it a last flicker of appetite. The remains of the autumn banquet are plentiful. The grub makes use of them no longer for greedy feasting, but just as a midnight snack between two slumbers, that of winter and the deeper sleep of the metamorphosis. Hence the sides of the sheath are attacked spasmodically. Breaches yawn, sections of wall come tumbling down, and soon the edifice is nothing but an unrecognizable ruin.

The lower portion of the original sausage remains, however, with its walls intact for a length of an inch or two. Here, in a thick layer, the grub's excreta are accumulated, held in reserve for the final work. In the centre of this mass a hollow is dug, carefully polished inside. With the excavated rubbish the grub builds not just a canopy, like that with which the winter alcove was protected, but a solid lid, with a rough outer surface, in appearance not unlike the work of the Cetoniæ when they wrap themselves in a shell of mould. This lid, with what is left of the pudding, forms a habitation which would remind us pretty closely of the Cockchafer's dwelling, were it not truncated in the upper part, which moreover is most often topped by a few remnants from the destroyed cylinder.

The grub is now shut in for the transformation, motionless, with its body emptied of all dross. In a few days a blister appears on the dorsal surface of the last abdominal segments. This swells, spreads and gradually extends as far as the thorax. It is the work of excoriation beginning. Distended by a colourless liquid, the blister gives an uncertain glimpse of a sort of milky cloud, the first blurred outline of the new organism.

The thorax splits in front, the cast skin is slowly pushed backwards, and at last we have the nymph, all white, half-opaque and half-crystalline. I obtain my first nymphs about the beginning of May.

Four or five weeks later, the perfect insect arrives, white on the wing-cases and belly, while the rest of the body already possesses the normal colouring. The chromatic evolution is quickly completed; and, before the end of June, the Geotrupes, now perfectly matured, emerges from the soil at twilight and flies off to start on his scavenger's job without delay. The laggards, those whose egg has gone through the winter, are still in the white nymphal stage when their elders effect their release. Not before September is nigh will they burst their natal shell and, in their turn, sally forth to aid in the cleansing of the fields.

1 The Rose-chafer, whose grub forms the prey of the Scolia-wasp. Cf. *The Life and Love of the Insect*: chap. xi.—*Translator's Note.*

CHAPTER XV
THE SISYPHUS: THE INSTINCT OF PATERNITY

The duties of paternity are hardly ever imposed on any except the higher animals. The bird excels in them; and the furred folk perform them honourably. Lower in the scale, the father is generally indifferent to his family. Very few insects form exceptions to this rule. Whereas all display a frenzied ardour in propagating their species, nearly all, having satisfied the passion of the moment, promptly break off domestic relations and retire, heedless of their brood, which must do the best that it can for itself.

This paternal coldness, which would be detestable in the higher ranks of the animal kingdom, where the weakness of the young demands prolonged assistance, has here as its excuse the robustness of the new-born insect, which is able unaided to gather its food, provided that it be in a propitious place. When all that the Pieris need do, to safeguard the prosperity of the race, is to lay her eggs on the leaves of a cabbage, what use would a father's solicitude be? The mother's botanical instinct requires no assistance. At laying-time, the other parent would be an obstacle. Let him go and flirt elsewhere; he would only be in the way at this critical season.

Most insects are equally summary in their educational methods. They have but to choose the refectory which will be the home of the family once it is hatched, or else a place that will allow their young to find suitable fare for themselves. There is no need for the father in these cases. After the wedding, therefore, the unoccupied male, henceforth useless, drags out a languid existence for a few days more and at last dies without lending the least assistance in the work of setting up his offspring in life.

Things do not always happen in quite such a primitive fashion. There are tribes that provide a dower for their families, that prepare board and lodging for them in advance. The Bees and Wasps, in particular, are masters in the industry of making cellars, jars and satchels in which the mess of honey for the young is hoarded; they are perfect in the art of creating burrows stocked with the game that forms the food of their grubs.

Well, this enormous labour, which is one of building and provisioning combined, this toil, in which the insect's whole life is spent, is done by the mother alone. It wears her out, it utterly exhausts her. The father, drunk with sunlight, stands by the edge of the workyard watching his plucky helpmate at her job and considers himself to have done all the work that he is called upon to do when he has toyed a little with his fair neighbours.

Why does he not lend the mother a helping hand? It is now or never. Why does he not follow the example of the Swallow couple, both of whom bring their bit of straw, their blob of mortar to the building, their Midge to the brood? He does nothing of the kind, perhaps alleging his comparative weakness as an excuse. It is a poor argument, for to cut a disk out of a leaf, to scrape some cotton from a downy plant, to collect a little bit of cement in muddy places would not overtax his strength. He could very easily help, at any rate as a labourer; he is quite fit to gather the materials for the mother, with her greater intelligence, to fix in place. The real reason of his inactivity is sheer ineptitude.

It is strange that the Hymenopteron, the most gifted of the industrial insects, should know nothing of paternal labour. The male, in whom one would think that the needs of the young ought to develop the highest aptitudes, remains as dull-witted as a Butterfly, whose family is established at so small a cost. The bestowal of instinct baffles our most reasonable conjectures.

It baffles them so thoroughly that we are extremely surprised when we find in the muck-raker the noble prerogative denied to the honey-gatherer. Various Dung-beetles are accustomed to help in the burden of housekeeping and know the value of working in double harness. Remember the Geotrupes couple, preparing their larva's portion together; think of the father lending his mate the assistance of his powerful press in the manufacture of the tight-packed sausages, a splendid example of domestic habits and one extremely surprising amid the general egoism.

To this example, hitherto unique, my constant studies of the subject enable me to-day to add three others, which are equally interesting; and all three are likewise furnished by the Dung-beetle guild. I will describe them, but briefly, for in many particulars their story is the same as that of the Sacred Beetle, the Spanish Copris and the others.

The first case is that of the Sisyphus (*S. Schæfferi*, Lin.), the smallest and most zealous of our pill-rollers. He is the liveliest and most agile of them all, recking nothing of awkward somersaults and headlong falls on the impossible tracks to which his obstinacy brings him back again and again. It was in memory of these wild gymnastics that Latreille gave him the name of Sisyphus, famous in the annals of Tartarus. The unhappy wretch had the terrible task of having to roll a huge stone up hill; and each time he had toiled to the top of the mountain the stone would slip from his grasp and roll to the bottom. Try again, poor Sisyphus, try again and go on trying: your punishment will not be over until the rock is firmly fixed up there.

I like this myth. It is in a fashion the history of a good many of us, not detestable scoundrels worthy of eternal torments, but decent, hard-working folk, doing their duty by their neighbours. They have one crime only to expiate: that of poverty. So far as I am concerned, for half a century and more I have painfully climbed that steep ascent, leaving garments stained with blood and sweat on its sharp crags; I have strained every nerve, drained myself dry, spent my strength recklessly in the struggle to hoist up to safety that crushing burden, my daily bread; and hardly is the loaf balanced when it slips off, slides down and is lost in the abyss. Try again, poor Sisyphus, try again until the load, falling for the last time, smashes your head and sets you free at last.

The Sisyphus of the naturalists knows none of these bitter trials. Untroubled by the steep slopes, he gaily trundles his load, at one time bread for himself, at another for his children. He is very scarce in these parts; and I should never have managed to procure a suitable number of subjects for my purpose, but for an assistant whom I ought to present to the reader, for he will play his part more than once in these narratives.

I speak of my son Paul, a little chap of seven. My assiduous companion on my hunting-expeditions, he knows better than any one of his age the secrets of the Cicada, the Locust, the Cricket and especially the Dung-beetle, his great delight. Twenty paces away, his sharp eyes will distinguish the real mound that marks a burrow from casual heaps of earth; his delicate ears catch the Grasshopper's faint stridulation, which to me remains silence. He lends me his sight and hearing; and I, in exchange, present him with ideas, which he receives attentively, raising wide, blue, questioning eyes to mine.

Oh, what an adorable thing is the first blossoming of the intellect; what a beautiful age is that when innocent curiosity awakens, enquiring into all things! So little Paul has his own vivarium, in which the Sacred Beetle makes pears for him; his own little garden, no larger than a pocket-handkerchief, where he grows beans, often digging them up to see if the tiny roots are growing longer; his forest plantation, in which stand four oaks a hand's-breadth high, still furnished on one side with the twin-breasted acorn that feeds them. It all makes a welcome change from dry grammar, which gets on none the worse for it.

What beautiful and delightful things natural history could put into children's heads if science would but stoop to charm the young; if our barracks of colleges would but add the living study of the fields to the lifeless study of books; if the red tape of the curriculum beloved by bureaucrats did not strangle any eager initiative! Little Paul, my boy, let us study as much as we can in the open country, among the rosemary- and arbutus-shrubs. By so doing, we shall gain in vigour of body and mind; we shall find more of the true and the beautiful than in any old musty books.

To-day we are giving the blackboard a rest; it is a holiday. We get up early, in view of the contemplated expedition, so early indeed that you will have to start without your breakfast. Have no fear: when your appetite comes, we will call a halt in the shade and you shall find in my bag the usual viaticum, an apple and a piece of bread. The month of May is near at hand; the Sisyphus must have appeared. What we have to do now is to explore, at the foot of the mountain, the lean meadows where the flocks have been; we shall have to break with our fingers, one by one, the cakes dropped by the Sheep and baked by the sun, but still retaining a kernel of crumb under their crust. There we shall find the Sisyphus huddled, waiting for the fresher windfall with which the evening grazers will supply him.

Instructed in this secret, which I learnt long ago from chance discoveries, little Paul forthwith becomes a master in the art of shelling Sheep-droppings. He displays such zeal and such an instinct for the best morsels that, after a very few halts, I am rich beyond my fondest hopes. Behold me the proud owner of six couples of Sisyphi, an unprecedented treasure, which I was far from expecting.

It will not be necessary to rear these in the vivarium. A wire-gauze cover is enough, with a bed of sand and a supply of victuals to their liking. They are so small, hardly the size of a cherry-stone! And so curious in shape withal! Dumpy body: the hinder end pointed; and very long legs, resembling a Spider's when outspread: the hind-legs are of inordinate length and curved, which is most useful for clasping and squeezing the pellet.

Pairing takes place about the beginning of May, on the surface of the ground, amid the remains of the cake on which the couple have been feasting. Soon the time comes for establishing the family. With equal zeal, husband and wife alike take part in kneading, carting and stowing away the bread for the children. With the cleaver of the fore-legs a morsel of the right size is cut from the lump placed at their disposal. Father and mother manipulate the piece together, giving it little pats, pressing it and fashioning it into a ball as large as a big pea.

As in the Sacred Beetle's workshop, the mathematically round shape is obtained without the mechanical trick of rolling the ball. The fragment is modelled into a sphere before it is moved, before it is even loosened from its support. Here again we have an expert in geometry familiar with the form that is best adapted to make preserved foodstuffs keep for a long time.

The pellet is soon ready. It must now, by vigorous rolling, be made to acquire the crust which will protect the crumb from too-rapid evaporation.

The mother, who can be recognized by her slightly larger size, harnesses herself in the place of honour, in front. With her long hind-legs on the ground and her fore-legs on the ball, she hauls it towards her backwards. The father pushes behind in the reverse position, head downwards. It is precisely the same method as the Sacred Beetle's, when working in twos, but with another object. The Sisyphus team convey a larva's dowry, whereas the big pill-rollers trundle a banquet which the two fortuitous partners will eat up underground.

The couple start, for no definite goal, across such impediments as the ground may present. These obstacles are impossible to avoid in this backward march; and, if they were perceived, the Sisyphus would not try to go round them, as witness her obstinacy in trying to climb the wirework of the cage. This is an arduous and impracticable enterprise. Clawing the meshes of the gauze with her hind-legs, the mother pulls the load towards her; then, putting her fore-legs round it, she holds it suspended. The father, finding nothing to stand upon, clings to the ball, encrusts himself in it, so to speak, adding his weight to that of the lump and taking no further pains. The effort is too great to last. The ball and its rider, forming one mass, fall to the floor. The mother, from above, looks for a moment in surprise and forthwith drops down to recover the load and renew her impossible attempt to scale the side. After repeated falls, the ascent is abandoned.

The carting on level ground is not effected without impediment either. At every moment the load swerves on the mound made by a bit of gravel; and the team topple over and kick about, with their bellies in the air. This is a trifle, the veriest trifle. The two pick themselves up and resume their positions as cheerily as ever. These tumbles, which so often fling the Sisyphus on his back, cause him no concern; one would even think that they were sought for. After all, the pill has to be matured, to receive consistency. And, under these conditions, bumps, blows, falls and jolts are all part of the programme. This mad steeplechasing goes on for hours.

At last the mother, regarding the work as completed, goes off a little way in search of a favourable site. The father mounts guard, squatting on the treasure. If his companion's absence be prolonged, he relieves his boredom by spinning the ball nimbly between his uplifted hind-legs. He juggles after a fashion with the precious pellet; he tests its perfection with the curved branches of his compasses. To see him frisking in that jubilant attitude, who can doubt his lively satisfaction as a *paterfamilias* assured of the future of his children?

'It's I,' he seems to say, 'it's I who kneaded this round, soft loaf; it's I who made this bread for my sons!'

And he lifts on high, for all to see, this magnificent testimonial to his industry.

Meanwhile, the mother has selected the site. A shallow pit is made, a mere beginning of the projected burrow. The ball is rolled near it. The father, that vigilant guardian, does not let go, while the mother digs with her legs and forehead. Soon the hollow is big enough to hold the pellet, the sacred thing which she insists on having quite close to her: she must feel it bobbing up and down behind her, on her back, safe from parasites, before she decides to go farther. She is afraid of what might happen to the little loaf if it were left on the threshold of the burrow until the home was completed. There are plenty of Aphodii and Midges to grab it. One cannot be too careful.

The pellet therefore is inserted, half in and half out of the partly-formed basin. The mother, underneath, gets her legs round it and pulls; the father, above, lets it down gently and sees that the hole is not choked up with falling earth. All goes well. The digging is resumed and the descent continues, always with the same caution, one of the Sisyphi pulling the load, the other regulating the drop and clearing away anything that might hinder the operation. A few more efforts; and the ball disappears underground with the two miners. What follows for some time to come can be only a repetition of what we have just seen. Let us wait half a day or so.

If we have kept careful watch, we shall see the father come up again to the surface by himself and crouch in the sand near the burrow. Detained below by duties in which her companion can be of no assistance to her, the mother usually postpones her appearance till the morrow. At last she shows herself. The father leaves the place where he was snoozing and joins her. The reunited couple go back to the heap of victuals, refresh themselves and then cut out another piece, on which again the two work together, both as regards the modelling and the carting and storing.

I am delighted with this conjugal fidelity. That it is really the rule I dare not declare. There must be flighty Beetles who, in the hurly-burly under a spreading cake, forget the first fair pastry-cook whom they helped with her baking and devote themselves to others, met by chance; there must be temporary couples, who divorce each other after producing a single pill. No matter: the little that I have seen gives me a high opinion of the Sisyphus' domestic habits.

Let us recapitulate these habits before passing on to the contents of the burrow. The father works just as hard as the mother at extracting and modelling the lump that is to constitute a larva's dowry; he shares in the carting, even though he plays a secondary part; he keeps watch over the loaf when the mother is absent looking for a spot at which to dig the burrow; he helps in the work of excavation; he carries outside the rubbish from the cavity; and lastly, to crown these good qualities, he is to a large extent faithful to his spouse.

The Scarabæus displays some of these characteristics. He readily helps in manipulating the pill; when it has to be carted, he takes his place in a team of two, one pulling and one pushing. But let me repeat that the motive of this mutual service is selfishness: the two fellow-workers labour and cart the lump only for their own purpose. To them it is a gala cake and nothing more. In that part of her work which concerns the family, the Scarabæus mother has no assistant. Alone she rounds her sphere, extracts it from the pile, rolls it backwards by herself in the head-downward posture adopted by the male of the Sisyphus couple; alone she digs her burrow; alone she stores away its contents. Heedless of the laying mother and the brood, the other sex does not assist at all in the exhausting task. How different from the pigmy pill-roller!

It is time to inspect the burrow. At no great depth we find a tiny niche, just large enough to allow the mother to move around her work. The smallness of the chamber tells us that the father cannot remain there for long. When the studio is ready, he must go away to leave the sculptress room to turn. We have already seen him coming back to the surface some time before the mother.

The contents of the cellar consist of a single pill, a masterpiece of plastic art. It is a copy of the Sacred Beetle's pear on a very much reduced scale, its smallness making the polish of the surface and the elegance of the curves all the more striking. Its main diameter varies between one-half and three-quarters of an inch. It is the most artistic achievement of the Dung-beetle's art.

But this perfection is of brief duration. Soon the pretty pear is covered with knotty excrescences, black and twisted, which disfigure it with their blotchy lumps. A part of the surface, otherwise intact, disappears beneath an amorphous mass of eruptions. The origin of these ugly warts baffled me at first. I suspected some fungous growth, some Sphæriacea, for instance, recognizable by its black and pimply crust. The larva showed me my mistake.

As usual, this is a grub bent into a hook and carrying on its back a large pouch or hump, the emblem of a ready evacuator. Like the Sacred Beetle's, indeed, it excels at stopping up any accidental holes in its shells with an instantaneous spray of stercoral cement, of which it always keeps a supply in its knapsack. It practises moreover an art of vermicelli-making which is unknown to the pill-rollers, except the Broad-necked Scarab, who however but seldom makes use of it.

The larvæ of the various Dung-beetles employ their digestive residues for plastering their cell, whose dimensions lend themselves to this method of riddance, without the necessity of opening temporary windows through which to expel the ordure. Whether because of insufficient space or for other reasons which escape me, the Sisyphus-larva, after allowing for the regulation coating of the interior, ejects the excess of its products outside.

Let us keep a close eye on a pear whose inmate is already growing fairly big. Sooner or later we shall see that the surface at one point is getting thinner and softer; and then, through the frail screen, there is a spurt of dark-green fluid, which subsides with corkscrew evolutions. One more wart has been formed. It will turn black as it dries.

What has happened? The larva has made a temporary breach in the wall of its shell; and through the ventilator, which is still covered with a thin veil, it has excreted the superfluous cement which it was unable to use indoors. It has evacuated through the wall. The window deliberately opened in no way affects the safety of the grub, as it is at once closed and hermetically sealed with the base of the spout, which is compressed by a stroke of the trowel. With a stopper so quickly placed in position the food will keep fresh however many holes are made in the body of the pear. There is no danger of the dry air entering.

The Sisyphus also seems to be aware of the peril which later, in torrid weather, would threaten her tiny pear, buried at so slight a depth. She is a very early arrival. She works in April and May, when the atmosphere is mild. In the first fortnight of July, before the terrible dog-days have arrived, her family burst their shells and go in search of the heap that will furnish them with board and lodging during the scorching time of the year. Then comes the brief spell of autumn revelry, followed by the withdrawal underground for the winter sleep, the awakening in spring, and lastly, to complete the cycle, the pill-rolling festival.

One more observation about the Sisyphus. My six pairs under the wire-gauze cover gave me fifty-seven inhabited pellets. This census shows an average of over nine births to each couple, a figure which the Sacred Beetle is far from reaching. To what cause are we to attribute this flourishing brood? I can see but one: the fact that the male works as well as the mother. Family burdens that would exceed the strength of one are not too heavy when there are two to bear them.

CHAPTER XVI
THE LUNARY COPRIS; THE BISON ONITIS

Smaller than the Spanish Copris and less particular about a mild climate, the Lunary Copris (*C. lunaris*, Lin.) will confirm what the Sisyphus has told us of the part played by the father's collaboration in the prosperity of the family. Our country districts cannot show his match for oddity of male attire. Like the other, he wears a horn on his forehead; in addition, he has an embattled promontory in the middle of his corselet and a halberd-point and a deep, crescent-shaped groove on his shoulders. The climate of Provence and the niggardly supply of food in a wilderness of thyme do not suit him. He wants a country that is less dry, with meadows where the patches of cattle-dung will supply him with plenty of provender.

Unable to reckon on the rare specimens which we meet here from time to time, I have stocked my insect-house with strangers sent from Tournon by my daughter Aglaé. When April comes, she conducts an indefatigable search at my request. Seldom have so many Cow-claps been lifted with the point of the sunshade; seldom have delicate fingers with so much affection broken the cakes on the pastures. I thank the heroine in the name of science!

Her zeal meets with due reward. I become the proud possessor of six couples, which are immediately installed in the insect-house where the Spanish Copris used to work last year. I serve up the national dish, the superlative loaf furnished by my neighbour's Cow. There is not a sign of home-sickness among the exiles, who bravely begin their labours under the mysterious shelter of the cake.

I make my first excavation in the middle of June and am delighted with what my knife gradually lays bare as it cuts up the soil in thin slices. Each couple has dug itself a splendid vaulted room in the sand, more spacious than any that the Sacred Beetle or the Spanish Copris ever showed me and with a bolder arch. The greatest breadth is fully six inches; but the ceiling is very low, rising to hardly two inches.

The contents correspond with the extravagant dimensions of the hall. They form a dish worthy of the wedding of Camacho the Rich, a cake as broad as one's hand, of no great thickness and varying in outline. I have found them oval-shaped, kidney-shaped, shaped like a Starfish, with short, thick rays, and long and pointed, like a Cat's tongue. These minor details represent the pastry-cook's fancies. The essential and constant fact is this: in the six bakeries of my insect-house, the sexes are always both present beside the lump of paste, which, after being kneaded according to rule, is now fermenting and maturing.

What does this long cohabitation prove? It proves that the father has taken part in digging the cellar, in storing the victuals gathered by separate armfuls on the threshold of the door, and in kneading all the scraps into a single lump, which is more likely to improve by keeping. Were he a useless, idle incubus, he would not stay there, he would go back to the surface. The father therefore is a diligent fellow-worker. His assistance even looks as if it ought to extend farther still. We shall see.

Dear insects, my curiosity has disturbed your housekeeping. But you were only starting, you were having your house-warming, so to speak. Perhaps you may be able to make good the damage which I have wrought. Let us try. I will restore the condition of the establishment by supplying fresh provisions. It is for you now to dig new burrows, to carry down the wherewithal to replace the cake of which I have robbed you, and afterwards to divide the lump, improved by time, into rations suited to the needs of your larvæ. Will you do all this? I hope so.

My faith in the perseverance of the sorely-tried couples is not disappointed. A month later, in the middle of July, I venture on a second inspection. The cellars have been rebuilt, as spacious as at first. Moreover, by this time they are padded with a soft lining of dung on the floor and on a part of the side-walls. The two sexes are still there; they will not separate until the rearing is completed. The father, who has less family-affection, or perhaps is more timid, tries to steal off by the back-way as the light enters the shattered dwelling; the mother, squatting on her precious pellets, does not budge. These pellets are oval-shaped plums, very like those of the Spanish Copris, but not quite so large.

Knowing how few compose the latter's collection, I am greatly surprised at the sight that now meets my eyes. In a single cell I count seven or eight ovoids, standing one against the other and lifting up their nippled tops, each with its hatching-chamber. Notwithstanding its size, the hall is cram-full; there is hardly room left for the two guardians to move about. It may be compared with a bird's nest containing its eggs and no empty spaces.

The comparison is inevitable. What indeed are the Copris' pills but eggs of another sort, in which the nutritive mass of the white and the yolk is replaced by a pot of preserved foodstuffs? Here the Dung-beetles rival the birds and even surpass them. Instead of producing from within themselves, merely by the mysterious processes of nature, that which will provide for the latter growth of their young, they are actively and openly industrious, and by dint of their own skill provide food for their grubs which will achieve the adult form without other assistance. They know nothing of the long and tortuous process of incubation; the sun is their incubator. They have not the continual worry of providing food, for they prepare this in advance and make only one distribution. But they never leave the nest. Their watch is incessant. Father and mother, those vigilant guardians, do not quit the house until the family is fit to sally forth.

The father's usefulness is manifest so long as there is a house to dig and wealth to amass; it is less evident when the mother is cutting up her loaf into rations, shaping her ovoids, polishing them and watching over them. Can it be that the cavalier also takes part in this delicate task, which would rather seem to be a feminine monopoly? Is he able, with his sharp leg, to slice up the cake, to remove from it the requisite quantity for a larva's sustenance and to round the piece into a sphere, thus shortening the work, which could be revised and perfected by the mother? Does he know the art of stopping up chinks, of repairing breaches, of soldering slits, of scraping pellets and clearing them of any dangerous vegetable matter? Does he show the brood the same attentions which the mother lavishes by herself in the burrows of the Spanish Copris? Here the two sexes are together. Do they both take part in bringing up the family?

I tried to obtain an answer by installing a couple of Lunary Copres in a glass jar screened by a cardboard sheath, which enabled me readily and quickly to produce light or darkness. When suddenly surprised, the male was perched upon the pellets almost as often as the female; but, whereas the mother would frequently go on with her ticklish nursery-work, polishing the pellets with the flat of her leg and feeling and sounding them, the father, more cowardly and less engrossed in his duties, would drop down as soon as the daylight was admitted and run away to hide in some corner of the heap. There is no way of seeing him at work, so quick is he to shun the unwelcome light.

Still, though he refused to display his talents on my behalf, his very presence on the top of the ovoids betrays them. Not for nothing was he in that uncomfortable attitude, so ill-adapted to an idler's slumbers. He was then watching like his companion, touching up the damaged parts, listening through the walls of the shells to find out how the youngsters were progressing. The little that I saw assures me that the father almost rivals the mother in domestic solicitude until the family is finally emancipated.

The offspring gain in numbers by this paternal devotion. In the Spanish Copris' mansion, where the mother alone resides, we find four nurselings at most, often two or three, sometimes only one. In that of the Lunary Copris, where the two sexes cohabit and help each other, we count as many as eight, twice the largest population of the other. The hard-working father enjoys a magnificent proof of his influence upon the fate of the household.

Apart from labour in common, this prosperity demands another condition without which the zeal of the couple would be ineffectual. Before everything, if you want a big family you must have enough to feed it on. Remember the victualling methods of the Copris-tribe generally. They do not, like the pill-rollers, go gathering here and there a booty which is rounded into a ball and subsequently rolled to the burrow; they settle immediately underneath the heap which they find, and there, without leaving the threshold of the house, carve themselves slices which they carry down singly to their store until they have collected enough.

The Spanish Copris, at least in my neighbourhood, handles the product of the Sheep. It is of high quality, but not plentiful, even when the purveyor's intestines are in their most generous mood. The whole of it, therefore, is packed into the cavern and the insect does not come out again, being kept underground by family-cares, even though there be but one youngster to attend to. The niggardly morsel as a rule supplies material only for two or three larvæ. Consequently the family is a small one, through the difficulty in procuring provisions.

The Lunary Copris works under different conditions. His part of the country provides the Cow-clap, that rich patch of dung in which the insect finds inexhaustible supplies of the food needed by a flourishing offspring. This prosperity is assisted by the size of the abode, whose ceiling, with its exceptional breadth, is able to shelter a number of pills that would never fit into the Spanish Copris' much less roomy burrow.

For lack of space at home and of a well-furnished flour-bin, the latter restricts the number of her children, which is sometimes reduced to one. Can this be due to impotence of the ovaries? No. I have shown in an earlier chapter that, given free scope and a well-spread table, the mother is capable of producing twice her usual family and more. I described how for the three or four ovoids I substituted a loaf kneaded with my paper-knife. By means of this artifice, which increased the space in the narrow enclosure of the jar and provided fresh materials for modelling, I obtained from the mother a family of seven in all. It was a magnificent result, but far inferior to that derived from the following experiment, which was better managed.

This time I take away the pellets as they are formed, all but one, so as not to discourage the mother by my kidnapping. If she found nothing at all left of her previous products, she might perhaps weary of her fruitless labour. When the main loaf, of her constructing, has all been used, I replace it with another, made by myself. I go on doing this, removing the ovoid that has just been completed and renewing the finished lump of food until the insect refuses to accept any more. For five or six weeks the sorely tried mother never loses her patience and each time begins all over again and perseveringly restocks her empty nursery. At last the dog-days arrive, the brutal season which arrests all life by its excessive heat and dryness. My loaves, however carefully made, are scorned. The mother, overcome with torpor, refuses to work. She buries herself in the sand, at the foot of the last pellet, and there, motionless, awaits the liberating September rain. The indefatigable creature has bequeathed me thirteen ovoids, each modelled to perfection, each supplied with an egg; thirteen, a number unparalleled in the Copris' annals; thirteen, ten more than the normal laying.

The proof is established: if the horned Dung-beetle strictly limits her family, it is not through penury of the ovaries, but through fear of famine.

Is it not thus that things happen in our country, which, the statisticians tell us, is threatened with depopulation? The clerk, the artisan, the civil servant, the workman, the small shopkeeper are a daily increasing multitude with us; and all of them, having hardly enough to live upon, refrain as far as possible from adding to the numbers gathered around their ill-furnished table. When bread is short, the Copris is not wrong in becoming almost a celibate. Why should we cast a stone at his imitators? The motive is one of prudence on either side. It is better to live alone than surrounded by hungry mouths. The man who feels strong enough to struggle with poverty for himself shrinks in dismay from the poverty of a crowded home.

In the good old days, the tiller of the soil, the peasant, the backbone of the nation, found that a numerous family added to his wealth. All used to work and bring their bit of bread to the frugal repast. While the eldest drove the team afield, the youngest, clad in his first pair of breeches, took the brood of Ducklings to the pond.1

These patriarchal ways are becoming rare. Progress sees to that. Of course, it is an enviable thing to scorch along on a bicycle, working your legs up and down like a distracted Spider; but there is a reverse to the medal: progress brings luxury, but creates expensive tastes. In my village, the commonest factory-girl, earning her ten-pence a day, sports on a Sunday sleeves puffed at the shoulders and feathers in her hat like the fine ladies'; she has a sunshade with an ivory handle, a padded chignon, patent-leather shoes, with open-work stockings and lace flounces. O Goose-girl, I in my short linen jacket dare not look at you as you pass my door on your Sunday parade along the high-road! You make me feel too small with your smart raiment.

The young men, on the other hand, are assiduous frequenters of the café, which is much more luxurious than the old-fashioned pot-house. Here they find vermouth, bitters, absinthe, amer Picon, in short the whole collection of stupefying drugs. Such tastes as these make the fields seem too humble and the soil too stubborn. Since the receipts no longer come up to the expenses, they leave the land for the town, which is better-suited, so they imagine, for money-making. Alas, saving is no more practicable there than here! The workshop, where opportunities of spending money lie in wait by the score, makes a man no richer than the plough. But it is too late: you have made your bed; and you remain a poverty-stricken townsman, in terror of paternity.

And yet this country, with its glorious climate, fertility, and geographical position, is invaded by a host of cosmopolitans, sharks and sharpers of every sort. Long ago, it used to attract the sea-roving Phœnicians; the peace-loving Greeks, who brought us the alphabet, the vine and the olive-tree; the Romans, those harsh rulers, who handed down to us barbarities very difficult to eradicate. Swooping on this rich prey came the Cymri, the Teutons, the Vandals, the Goths, the Huns, the Burgundians, the Suevi, the Alani, the Franks, the Saracens, hordes driven hither by every wind that blows. And all this heterogeneous mixture was melted down and absorbed by the Gallic nation.

To-day the foreigner is stealthily making his way into our midst. We are threatened with a second barbarian invasion, peaceful, it is true, but yet disturbing. Will our language, so clear and so harmonious, become an obscure jargon, harsh with exotic gutturals? Will our generous character be dishonoured by rapacious hucksters? Will the land of our fathers cease to be a country and become a caravanserai? There is a fear of it, unless the old Gallic blood runs swift and strong once more and engulfs the stream of invaders.

Let us hope that it may be so and let us listen to what the horned Dung-beetle has to teach us. A large family demands food. But progress brings new needs, which cost much to satisfy; and our revenues are far from increasing at the same rate. When men have not enough for six or five or four, they are content to live as a family of three or two, or even to remain single. Guided by such principles as these, a nation, in its successive stages of progress, is on the road to suicide.

Let us go back then to where we were, suppress our artificial needs, those unwholesome fruits of a hot-house civilization, honour rustic frugality once again and remain on the land, where we shall find the soil bountiful enough to satisfy us if we moderate our desires. Then and not till then will the family flourish once more; then will the peasant, delivered from the town and its temptations, be our salvation.

The third Dung-beetle that has shown me the gift of paternal instinct is likewise a stranger. He comes to me from near Montpellier. He is the Bison Onitis, or, according to others, the Bison Bubas. Taking no interest in nomenclature subtleties, I shall not choose between the two generic names, but will retain the specific denomination of Bison, which has the sound which Linnæus wanted. I made his acquaintance many years ago in the country around Ajaccio,2 among the saffrons and cyclamens that bloom so sweetly under the shade of the myrtles. Come hither and let me admire you yet once again, O beauteous insect! You recall my youthful enthusiasm on the shores of the glorious gulf, so rich in shell-fish. Far was I from suspecting at the time that it would one day fall to my share to sing your praises! I have not seen you since. Welcome to my vivarium! And now tell us something about yourself.

You are a sturdy little chap, short-legged and packed into a solid rectangle, a sign of strength. On your head you wear two abbreviated horns, curved like a Steer's; and you prolong your corselet into a blunt forehead adorned with two pretty dimples, one on the right and one on the left. Your general appearance and your male finery make you a near neighbour of the coprinary group. The entomologists, in fact, class you immediately after the Copres and a long way from the Geotrupes. Does your trade tally with the place which the systematists allot to you? What can you do?

In common with others, I admire the classifier who, studying the mouth, the legs and the antennæ in the dead insect, is sometimes happy in his grouping and able, for instance, to include in the same family the Scarab and the Sisyphus, who differ so greatly in appearance and so little in habits. Yet this method, which ignores the higher manifestations of life in order to pore over the smallest details of the corpse, too often misleads us as to the insect's real talent, which is a much more important characteristic than a joint more or less in the antennæ. The Bison, like many others, warns us to be careful where we are going. Though akin to the Copris in structure, he is much nearer the Geotrupes in his industry. Like them, he packs sausages in a cylindrical mould; like them again, he has the paternal instinct.

I inspect my one couple in the middle of June. Under a plentiful pile provided by the Sheep is a perpendicular shaft a finger's-breadth in diameter, open freely throughout its length and running some nine inches down. The bottom of this well branches out into five different galleries, each occupied by a roly-poly pudding similar to the Geotrupes', but less bulky and not so long. The mass of fodder has a warty surface, is rounded off clumsily and has a hatching-chamber scooped out of it at the lower end. This chamber is a little round cell, coated with a semifluid wash. The egg is oval, white and comparatively large, as is the rule among Dung-beetles. In short, the Bison's rustic work is a very close reproduction of the Geotrupes'.

I am disappointed: I expected better things. The insect's elegance seemed to promise something more artistic, a finer craftsmanship, skilled in the modelling of pears, gourds, balls and ovoids. Once again, be careful how you judge animals, any more than men, by appearances. The structure gives us no idea of the insect's all-round ability.

I surprise the couple at the cross-roads where the five blind-alleys, the sausages, start. The intrusion of the light has frightened them into immobility. Before the disturbance caused by my excavations, what were the two faithful partners doing at this spot? They were watching over the five cells, ramming down the last column of provisions, completing it with new contributions of material, brought down from above and taken from the heap that forms a cover to the shaft. They were perhaps preparing to dig a sixth chamber, if not more, and to stock it like the others. I realize at any rate that there must be many ascents from the bottom of the pit to the rich warehouse on the surface, whence the bundles of material are carried down in the legs of the one to be methodically pressed on top of the egg by the other.

The shaft indeed is open throughout its length. Moreover, to prevent the crumbling of the walls which would result from frequent journeys, the sides are plastered with stucco from end to end. This coat is made of the same material as the puddings and is more than a twenty-fifth of an inch thick. It is continuous and fairly even, without having too elaborate a finish. It keeps the surrounding earth in place, so much so that big fragments of the tunnel can be removed without losing their shape.

In the hamlets on the Alps, the south fronts of the buildings are coated with Cow-dung, which, after drying in the summer sun, becomes the winter fuel. The Bison knows this pastoral method, but practises it with another object: he hangs his house with manure to keep it from crumbling. The father might well be entrusted with this work in the intervals of rest which the mother leaves him while she is busy in the ticklish work of making her pudding layer by layer. The Geotrupes, by way of yet another industrial resemblance, has already shown us a similar consolidating plaster. Hers, it is true, is less regular and less complete.

After being ousted by my curiosity, the Bison couple set to work again and, by the middle of July, supplied me with three more puddings, making a total of eight. This time I find my two captives dead, one on the surface, the other in the ground. Can it be an accident? Or is it not more likely that the Bison constitutes an exception to the longevity of the Scarabs, Copres and others, who behold their offspring and even fly away to their second wedding in the following spring?

I incline to the belief that we come back here to the general insect law of a short life deprived of the chief joy of parenthood, the sight of one's children, for no regrettable incident happened, so far as I know, in the vivarium. If I am right in my conjectures, why does the Bison, though a near kinsman of the Copris, who attains a green old age, die so quickly, like the common herd, once the future of his family is assured? Here again we have an unsolved mystery.

A rapid sketch of the larva is preferable to long descriptions of its jaws and palpi, which make dull reading. I shall have said enough, I think, on the subject if I mention that it is bent into a crook, that it carries a knapsack on its back, that it is a quick evacuator and that it is clever at stopping up any cracks in the dwelling: characteristics and talents which are a general rule among the Dung-beetles. In August, when the pudding has been consumed in the middle and has become something of a ruin, the grub retires to the lower end and here isolates itself from the remainder of the cavity by means of a spherical enclosure, of which the mortar-bag supplies the materials.

The work, a graceful sphere about the size of a large cherry, is a masterpiece of stercoral architecture and may be compared with that which the Bull Onthophagus has already shown us. Little nodes, arranged in concentric lines and alternating like the tiles of a roof, adorn the object from pole to pole. Each of them must correspond with a stroke of the trowel putting its load of mortar in place. If you did not know what it was, you would take the thing for the chiselled kernel of some tropical fruit. A sort of rough pericarp completes the illusion. It is the rind of the pudding which surrounds the central jewel but is easily removed, just as the husk separates from the nut. When we have done the shelling, we are quite surprised to find this splendid kernel under its rustic wrapper.

Such is the chamber built with a view to the metamorphosis. The larva spends the winter there in a state of torpor. I hoped to obtain the adult insect in the spring. To my great surprise, the larval stage continued until the end of July. It takes about a year, therefore, for the nymph to make its appearance.

This slowness in maturing surprises me. Can it be the rule in the open fields? I think so, for in the confinement of my insect-house nothing happened, to my knowledge, that would occasion this delay. I therefore enter the result of my manœuvres without any fear of making a mistake: lying lifeless in its elegant and solid casket, the larva of the Bison Onitis takes twelve months to develop into a nymph, whereas those of the other Dung-beetles effect their transformation in a few weeks. As to stating or even suspecting the cause of this strange larval longevity, these are points which must be left in the limbo of the unexplained.

Softened by the September rains, the stercoral shell, until now as hard as a plum-stone, yields to the hermit's thrust; and the adult Beetle comes up into the light of day to lead a life of revelry so long as the mild atmosphere of the last days of summer permits. When the first cold weather sets in, he retires to his winter quarters underground and reappears in the spring to begin the cycle of life all over again.

1 Cf. Fabre's own youthful experiences, in *The Life of the Fly*: chap. vii.—*Translator's Note.*

2 For the author's stay at Ajaccio, where he was a schoolmaster in his youth, cf. *The Life of the Fly*: chap. vi.—*Translator's Note.*

CHAPTER XVII
THE BULL ONTHOPHAGUS: THE CELL

Begun to-day and dropped to-morrow, taken up again later and again abandoned, according to the chances of the day, the study of instinct makes but halting progress. The changing seasons bring unwelcome delays, forcing the observer to wait till the following year or even longer for the answer to his eager questions. Moreover, the problem often crops up unexpectedly, as the result of some casual incident of slight interest in itself, and it comes in a form so vague that it gives little basis for precise investigation. How can one investigate what has not yet been suspected? We have no facts to go upon and are consequently unable to tackle the problem frankly.

To collect these facts by fragments, to subject those fragments to varied tests in order to try their value, to make them into a sheaf of rays lighting up the darkness of the unknown and gradually causing it to emerge: all this demands a long space of time, especially as the favourable periods are brief. Years elapse; and then very often the perfect solution has not appeared. There are always gaps in our sheaf of light; and always behind the mysteries which the rays have penetrated stand others, still shrouded in darkness.

I am perfectly aware that it would be preferable to avoid repetitions and to give a complete story every time; but, in the domain of instinct, who can claim a harvest that leaves no grain for other gleaners? Sometimes the handful of corn left on the field is of more importance than the reaper's sheaves. If we had to wait until we knew every detail of the question studied, no one would venture to write the little that he knows. From time to time, a few truths are revealed, tiny pieces of the vast mosaic of things. Better to divulge the discovery, however humble it be. Others will come who, also gathering a few fragments, will assemble the whole into a picture ever growing larger but ever notched by the unknown.

And then the burden of years forbids me to entertain long hopes. Distrustful of the morrow, I write from day to day, as I make my observations. This method, one of necessity rather than choice, sometimes results in the reopening of old subjects, when new investigations throw light within and enable me to complete or it may be to modify the first text.

Years ago, I obtained a few noteworthy particulars about the Onthophagi, thanks to a very rough and ready method of rearing a few of them jumbled up with other Beetles in whom I was more interested. One of the earlier volumes gives a rapid sketch of them.1 The results, hurriedly and almost fortuitously acquired, inspired me with a wish to observe systematically and closely the habits, industry and development of an insect which I had already introduced to the reader in too summary a fashion. Let us speak once more of the Onthophagi, that nation of little horned dung-worshippers.

Lately, I have reared the following species, according as I chanced to pick them up: *Onthophagus taurus*, Linn., *O. vacca*, Linn., *O furcatus*, Fabr., *O. Schreberi*, Linn., *O. nuchicornis*, Linn., *O. lemur*, Fabr. There has been no choice on my part; I accept all that present themselves in sufficient numbers. The first especially abound. I am delighted, for the Bull Onthophagus is the chief of the clan. There is none to equal him, if not in dress, for this may be a richer copper in the others, at least in the handsome horns which are the masculine prerogative. He will be the object of special attention in my menagerie. For the rest, as what he teaches me is repeated elsewhere without noteworthy variations, his history will be that of the whole tribe.

I capture him, as well as the others, in the course of May. At this period of genetic awakening, I find them swarming very busily under the Sheep-droppings, not those which are moulded into olives and scattered in trails, but those which are ejected in slabs of some size. The first are too dry and too scanty and the Onthophagus thinks nothing of them; the second are goodly messes and he works them in preference to any other material.

The Mule's copious heap is also largely utilized; but it is very stringy and, though the Beetle finds plenty in it for his own feasts, he very seldom uses it for his offspring. Where the nests are concerned, the Sheep is the main purveyor. Her exceptionally plastic product at once attracts the custom of the Onthophagi, who are just as dainty epicures as the Sacred Beetle, the Copris or the Sisyphus. If, however, the ovine pottage be lacking, they fall back upon the coarser lump of the Mule, with the aid of a scrupulous selection.

There is no difficulty about bringing up Onthophagi. A spacious vivarium that lends itself to frolicsome sports is not necessary here; it would even be inconvenient and would not favour close observation, because of the tumult prevailing in a numerous and varied crowd. I prefer a number of separate establishments, simpler and smaller, which I can carry into my private workroom. They will lend themselves better to assiduous inspection, without putting me to the trouble of digging. What receptacles shall I choose?

There are certain glass pots fitted with a tin lid which you screw over their mouths. They are used for honey, preserved fruits, jam, jelly and similar products dear to the heart of *materfamilias* when the winter scarcity sets in. I procure a dozen of these by clearing the cupboard in which the preserves are kept. They hold, on the average, about a pint and three-quarters.

Half-filled with fresh sand and supplied in addition with provisions obtained from the Sheep's pastry-shop, each jar receives its share of Onthophagi, of separate species and with both sexes present. When the glass houses are used up and the population becomes too dense, I resort to ordinary flower-pots, furnished according to rule and closed with a pane of glass. The whole collection is arranged on my large laboratory-table. My captives are satisfied with their installation, which provides them with a mild temperature, a nicely-shaded light and first-class fare.

What more is needed to complete the Dung-beetles' happiness? Nothing but the raptures of pairing. They indulge in these freely. Interned in the second half of May, with not a thought to the new state of things which puts a stop to their frolics among the thyme, eagerly they seek one another out, make their overtures and group themselves in couples.

This is an excellent occasion to find the reply to a primary question: do the Onthophagus father and mother work in conjunction when looking after the brood; have they a permanent household, similar to that which we have seen in the Geotrupes, the Sisyphus and the Minotaur;2 or is the mating followed by a sudden and definite rupture? The Bull Onthophagus shall tell us.

I delicately transfer two insects in the act of coupling and establish them in another, separate jar, provided with victuals and fresh sand. The moving is performed safely; the entwined pair remain united. A quarter of an hour afterwards, they separate; the great job is finished. The food is close at hand. They refresh themselves for a moment; and then each, without bothering in the least about the other, digs his burrow and buries himself in solitude.

A week or so passes. The male reappears on the surface; he is restless, he makes desperate efforts to climb out; the relations are done, quite done; he wants to get away. By and by, the female comes up in her turn; she tries the nearest cake, picks the best of it and takes it underground. She is building her nest. As to her companion, he does not even notice what is happening: these things do not concern him.

The other captives, of no matter what species, when consulted in the same manner, give the same reply. The Onthophagus tribe knows nothing of household ties.

In what respect are those who know them and who observe them so faithfully any the better off? I do not quite see; or, to be more candid, I do not see at all. If, in the case of the Geotrupes, I see in the bulky pudding some slight excuse for the collaboration of the father, who is a valuable assistant in the fabrication of this kind of preserve, and if, in that of the Minotaur, the immensely deep well might suggest to me the need for the trident-wearing helper, who shoots out the rubbish while the mother goes on digging, I should still be without an explanation when I came to the Sisyphus, who is very economical both in provisions and in the labour of excavation and requires no help with either. I will not deny that, in this last case, the male is of some use, watching over the pill, lending occasional help and encouraging the female with his presence; but, after all, the part which he plays as a collaborator is a very secondary one, and the mother, one would say, could do without any assistance, as is the rule among the Scarabæi. Here, besides, we have the Bull Onthophagus, who is even smaller than the Sisyphus; and this dwarf, unacquainted with a partnership that would increase her powers twofold, fulfils a task which is almost equivalent to that of the Beetles who roll their pills in double harness.

Then how are talents and industries distributed? If we go on accumulating fact upon fact, observation upon observation, shall we ever come to know? I venture to doubt it.

I have friends who sometimes say to me:

'Now that you have collected such a mass of details, you ought to follow up analysis with synthesis and promulgate a comprehensive theory of the origin of instincts.'

There's a rash proposal for you! Because I have turned over a few grains of sand on the seashore, am I qualified to talk about the ocean depths? Life has its unfathomable secrets. Human knowledge will be struck off the world's records before we know all that is to be said about a Gnat.

Equally obscure is the question of nest-building. By a nest we understand any residence constructed purposely to receive the eggs and to protect the development of the young. The Bees and Wasps excel in the art. They know how to make cabins out of cotton-stuffs, wax, leaves or resin; they build turrets of clay and domes of masonry; they mould earthenware urns. The Spiders vie with them. Remember the flying-machines, the rose-patterned paraboloids of certain Epeiræ; the globular bag of the Lycosa; the Labyrinth Spider's cloisters with their Gothic arches; the Clotho Spider's tent and lentiform pockets.3

The Locust makes pits surmounted by a frothy chimney; the Mantis whips her glair into a frothy mass.4 The Fly and the Butterfly, on the other hand, know nothing of these fond attentions: they limit themselves to laying their eggs at spots where the young can find board and lodging for themselves.5 The Beetle also is generally extremely ignorant of the finer points of nest-building. By a very singular exception, the Dung-beetles, alone among the immense host of wearers of armoured wing-cases, have a special art of rearing, a system of upbringing which can bear comparison with that of the most gifted insects. How did they come by this industry?

Venturesome minds, deluded by the greatly daring theorists, tell us that the science of the future, rich in evidence drawn from the mysteries of fibre and cell, will draw up an affiliation-table in which the animal kingdom will be classified so that the place occupied by a creature shall inform us of its instincts, without any need of preliminary observation. We shall determine the aptitudes by means of learned formulæ, even as numbers are determined by their logarithms. It is most impressive; but beware: we are dealing with Dung-beetles; let us consult them before we draw up the logarithmic table of instincts. The Onthophagus is related to the Copris, the Scarab and the Sisyphus, all of whom are versed in the art of making shapely pellets. Let us try to tell beforehand, according to the place which she occupies in the insect-table, going merely by the formula, what she is able to do in the way of nest-building.

She is small, I agree; but littleness does not diminish talent in the least, as witness the Titmouse, with his pendulous nest, the Wren and the Canary, who, although among the smallest of our little birds, are incomparable artists. The near kinswomen of the Onthophagus excel in making beautiful ovoids and pear-shaped gourds. She herself, so tiny and so precise, ought to do even better.

Well, the table deceives us, the formula lies: the Onthophagus is a very indifferent artist; her nest is a rudimentary piece of work, hardly fit to be acknowledged. I obtain it in profusion from the six species which I have brought up in my jars and flower-pots. The Bull Onthophagus alone provides me with nearly a hundred; and I find no two precisely alike, as pieces should be that come from the same mould and the same workshop.

To this lack of exact similarity, we must add inaccuracy of shape, now more now less accentuated. It is easy, however, to recognize among the bulk the pattern upon which the clumsy nest-builder works. It is a sack shaped like a thimble and standing erect, with the spherical thimble-end at the bottom and the circular opening at the top.

Sometimes the insect establishes itself in the central region of my apparatus, in the heart of the earthy mass; then, the resistance being the same in every direction, the sack-like shape is pretty accurate. But, generally, the Onthophagus prefers a solid basis to a dusty support and builds on the walls of the jar, especially on the bottom. When the support is vertical, the sack is a longitudinal section of a short cylinder, with the smooth flat surface against the glass and a rugged convexity every elsewhere. If the support be horizontal, as is most frequently the case, the cabin is a sort of undecided oval lozenge, flat at the bottom, bulging and vaulted at the top. To the general inaccuracy of these contorted shapes, regulated by no very definite pattern, we must add the coarseness of the surfaces, all of which, with the exception of the parts touching the glass, are covered with a crust of sand.

The manner of procedure explains this uncouth exterior. As laying-time draws nigh, the Onthophagus bores a cylindrical pit and descends underground to a moderate depth. Here, working with her forehead, her chin and her fore-legs, which are toothed like a rake, she forces back and heaps around her the materials which she has moved, so as to obtain as best she may a nest of suitable size.

The next thing is to cement the crumbling walls of the cavity. The insect climbs back to the surface by way of its pit; it gathers on its threshold an armful of mortar taken from the cake whereunder it has elected to set up house; it goes down again with its burden, which it spreads and presses upon the sandy wall. Thus it produces a concrete casing, the gravel of which is supplied by the wall itself and the cement by the produce of the Sheep. After a few trips and repeated strokes of the trowel, the pit is plastered on every side; the walls, encrusted all over with grains of sand, are no longer liable to give way.

The cabin is ready: it now wants only a tenant and stores. First, a large free space is made at the bottom: the hatching-chamber, where the egg is laid on the wall. Next comes the collecting of the provisions intended for the grub, a collecting done with scrupulous care. Recently, when building, the insect worked upon the outside of the doughy mass and took no notice of the earthy blemishes. Now, it penetrates to the very centre of the lump, through a gallery that looks as though it were made with a punch. When trying a cheese, the buyer employs a scoop, the hollow, cylindrical taster which is driven well in and pulled out with a sample taken from the middle of the cheese. The Onthophagus, when collecting for her grub, goes to work as though equipped with one of these tasters. She bores an exactly round hole into the piece which she is exploiting; she goes straight to the middle, where the material, not being exposed to the contact of the air, has kept more savoury and pliable. Here and here alone are gathered the armfuls which, gradually stowed away, kneaded and heaped up to the requisite extent, fill the sack to the top. Lastly, a plug of the same mortar, the sides of which are made partly of sand and partly of stercoral cement, roughly closes the cell, in such a way that an external inspection does not allow one to distinguish front from back.

To judge of the work and its merit, we must open it. A large empty space, oval in shape, occupies the rear end. This is the birth-chamber, huge in dimensions compared with its contents, the egg fixed on the wall, sometimes at the bottom of the cell and sometimes on the side. This egg is a tiny white cylinder, rounded at each tip and measuring a millimetre6 in length immediately after it is laid. With no other support than the spot on which the oviduct has planted it, it stands on its hinder end and projects into space.

A more or less enquiring glance is quite surprised to find so small a germ contained in so large a box. What does the tiny egg want with all that room? When carefully examined within, the walls of the chamber suggest another question. They are coated with a fine greenish pap, semifluid and shiny, the appearance of which does not agree with either the external or the internal aspect of the lump from which the insect has extracted its materials. A similar lime-wash is observed in the nest which the Scarab, the Copris, the Sisyphus, the Geotrupes and other makers of stercoraceous preserves contrive in the very heart of the provisions, to receive the egg; but nowhere have I seen it so plentiful, in proportion, as in the hatching-chamber of the Onthophagus. Long puzzled by this brothy wash, of which the Sacred Beetle provided me with the first instance, I at one time took the thing for a layer of moisture oozing from the bulk of the victuals and collecting on the surface of the enclosure without other effort than capillary action. That was the interpretation of this varnish which I accepted in various earlier passages.

I was wrong. The truth is something much more remarkable. To-day, better informed by the Onthophagus, I reopen the question: is this lime-wash, this semifluid cream, the result of a natural oozing, or is it the product of maternal foresight? A simple and conclusive experiment will give us the answer. I ought to have made it at the outset. I did not think of it, because the simple is usually the last thing that we call to our aid. Here is the experiment.

I pack a little glass jar, the size of a Hen's egg, with Sheep-dung as employed by the Onthophagus. With a glass rod, which leaves a perfectly smooth impression, I make a cylindrical cavity in the heap about an inch deep. After withdrawing the rod, I cover the orifice with a slab of the same material; and I protect the whole against desiccation by means of an hermetically closed lid. It is the Sacred Beetle's pear, with its hatching-chamber, on a larger scale; it is the Onthophagus' thimble, enormously exaggerated. I may say that, after the withdrawal of the glass rod, the surface of the cavity is a dull, greenish black, with not a trace of extravasated shiny moisture. If an oozing by capillary action really takes place, the semifluid varnish will appear; if nothing of the kind should occur, the surface will remain dull.

I wait a couple of days to allow the capillary sweating to take effect, if such a process there be. Then I examine the cavity. There is no shiny wash on the walls; they look as dull and dry as at the beginning. Three days later, I make a fresh inspection. Nothing has changed: the pit made by the glass rod shows no sign of exudation; it is even a little drier. So capillary action and its extravasations have nothing to do with the matter.

What then is the lime-wash that is found in every cell? The answer is inevitable: it is something produced by the mother, a special gruel, a milk-food elaborated for the benefit of the new-born grub.

The young Pigeon puts his beak into that of his parents, who, with convulsive efforts, force down his gullet first a casein mash secreted in the crop and later a broth of grains softened by being partly digested. He is fed upon disgorged foods, which are kind to the frailty and inexperience of a young stomach. The grub of the Onthophagus is brought up in much the same way, at the start. To assist its first attempts at swallowing, the mother prepares for it, in her crop, a light and strengthening cream.

To pass the dainty from mouth to mouth is impossible in her case: the construction of new cells keeps her busy elsewhere. Moreover—and this is a more serious point—the laying takes place egg by egg, at very long intervals, and the hatching is pretty slow: time would fail, had the family to be brought up in the manner of the Pigeons. Another method is perforce required. The infants' food is disgorged all over the walls of the cabin, in such a way that the nurseling finds itself surrounded with an abundance of bread and jam, in which the bread, the meat for the strong, is represented by the uncooked material, as supplied by the Sheep, while the jam, the food for the babe, is represented by the same material daintily prepared beforehand in the mother's stomach. We shall see the grub presently lick first the jam all around it and then stoutly attack the bread. One of our own children would behave no otherwise.

I should have liked to catch the mother in the act of disgorging and spreading her broth. I did not succeed in doing so. The proceedings take place in a tiny niche; and the busy cook blocks out the view. Also her fluster at being exhibited in broad daylight at once arrests the work.

If direct observation be lacking, at least the appearance of the material and the result of my experiment with the glass rod speak very plainly and tell us that the Onthophagus, here rivalling the Pigeon, but with a different method, disgorges the first mouthfuls for her sons. And the same may be said of the other Dung-beetles skilled in the art of building a hatching-chamber in the centre of the provisions.

No elsewhere in the insect world, except among the Bees, who prepare disgorged food in the shape of honey, is such solicitude seen. The dung-workers edify us with their morals. Several of them practise association in couples and found a household; several anticipate the process of suckling, that supreme expression of maternal tenderness, by turning their crop into a nipple. Life has its freaks. It settles amid ordure the creatures most highly endowed with domestic qualities. True, from there it mounts, with a sudden flight, to the sublime virtues of the bird.

Among the Onthophagi the egg grows considerably larger after it is laid; it almost doubles its linear dimensions, thus increasing the bulk eightfold. This growth is general among the Dung-beetles. If you note the size of an egg recently laid by any species and measure it again when the grub is about to be born, you will be quite surprised at the singular progress which it has made. The Sacred Beetle's egg, for instance, which at first is lodged pretty spaciously in its hatching-chamber, swells until it nearly fills the cavity.

The first idea that occurs to the mind is a very simple and tempting one, namely, that the egg feeds. Surrounded by strongly-flavoured effluvia, it becomes impregnated with emanations which distend its flexible tunic; it grows by a sort of alimentary respiration, just as a seed swells in fertile soil. That is how I pictured things at the beginning, when the delicate problem presented itself for the first time. But is this really what happens? Ah, if it were enough, when we were in need of food, to stand outside a cook-shop and inhale the smell of the good things that were being prepared inside, what a different world it would seem, to many of us! It would be too lovely!

The Onthophagus, the Copris and the other Beetles with cream-washed hatching-chambers are a delusion and a snare to us, with their eggs which are so ready to swell. The Minotaurus tells me so, somewhat late in the day; she compels me to reconsider my earlier interpretations entirely. Her egg is not enclosed in a hollow inside the victuals whose emanations might explain its growth; it is outside the sausage, a good way underneath, surrounded by sand on every side; and nevertheless it increases in size just as well as those lodged in a succulent cabin.

Moreover, the new-born grub surprises me by its chubbiness; it is seven or eight times as big as the egg whence it comes; the contents vastly exceed the capacity of the container. Besides, before touching the food from which it is separated by a ceiling of sand, the grub for a certain time continues its strange growing, as though new materials were being added to those which came out of the egg.

Here, in the dry sand, it is impossible to talk of effluvia capable of providing the wherewithal for the grub to wax big and fat. Then to what do both the egg and the new-born grub owe their growth? The Languedocian Scorpion7 gives us an excellent clue. When passing from a sort of larval stage to the final form, which is the same as that of the adult, we have seen him suddenly double his length and consequently increase eightfold in bulk before taking the least scrap of nourishment. A highly complex process of co-ordination and adjustment takes place in the interior of the organism; and the dimensions increase without the addition of new material.

An animal is a structure capable of becoming more spacious with the same amount of materials. Everything depends upon the molecular architecture, which becomes more and more refined by the tremors of life. The contents of the egg, a compact mass, expand into a creature which is all the bulkier for its richness in organs for diverse functions. Even so, the locomotive engine, the creature of industry, occupies more space than the iron, its raw material, melted down into a single ingot.

When the shell is able to stretch, the egg swells under the thrust of its contents, which form into an organic whole and dilate. This is the case with the various Dung-beetles. When the shell is hard and rigid, a void is made by evaporation at the thick end; and this excess of space supplies the room necessary for the increase in volume of the contents. This is the case with the birds, which develop within a chalky enclosure that does not alter in size. Both of them dilate, with this difference that the soft shell allows the inside work to be perceived outside, whereas the stiff shell reveals nothing.

Lastly, the hatching does not always stop the growth that is not preceded by feeding. For a little while longer the larva continues to increase in size; it completes the work of acquiring stability in its new equilibrium, the equilibrium of a living creature; it improves its physique by supplementary stretching. The Scorpion has already told us this; the grub of the Minotaurus and many others assure us of the same thing. It is, on a smaller scale, what we saw before in the Locust's wing,8 which, issuing from a very small sheath, soon unfurls into a sail of generous breadth.

Twice, therefore, am I changing my opinions in this history of the Dung-beetles: first, on the subject of the paste spread on the walls of the natal chamber; secondly, on the subject of the egg that increases in size after it is laid. I have corrected my statements without being greatly ashamed of my mistakes, for it is difficult indeed to reach the vein of truth at the first tentative boring. There is only one means of never blundering, which is never to do anything and, above all, to let ideas alone.

1 Chapter XI. of the present book appeared in the fifth volume of the *Souvenirs entomologiques*; this and the

following chapter formed part of the tenth and last volume.—*Translator's Note.*

2 Cf. *The Life and Love of the Insect*: chap. x.—*Translator's Note.*

3 For the Epeiræ, or Garden Spiders, the Lycosa, or Black-bellied Tarantula, and the Labyrinth and Clotho Spiders, cf. *The Life of the Spider*, by J. Henri Fabre, translated by Alexander Teixeira de Mattos: *passim.*—*Translator's Note.*

4 Cf. *The Life of the Grasshopper*: chaps. viii., ix., xvi. and xvii.—*Translator's Note.*

5 Cf. *The Life of the Fly* and *The Life of the Caterpillar*: *passim.*—*Translator's Note.*

6 ·039 inch.—*Translator's Note.*

7 Cf. *The Life and Love of the Insect*: chaps. xvii. and xviii. The seven essays on the Languedocian Scorpion will be included in the last volume of this complete edition of Fabre's entomological works.—*Translator's Note.*

8 Cf. *The Life of the Grasshopper*: chap. xix.—*Translator's Note.*

CHAPTER XVIII
THE BULL ONTHOPHAGUS: THE LARVA; THE NYMPH

May is the nesting-month of the different Onthophagi and of the Bull Onthophagus in particular. The mothers now go underground to some little depth, under the shelter of the cave whence the building and victualling-materials are extracted. Unaided by the males, who, heedless of family cares, continue to lead a life of jollity, they fashion their cabins and stuff them with provisions after the egg is laid. The work, for that matter, is crude and elementary and hardly needs the collaboration of the horned dandies. Five or six establishments at most, each founded in a couple of days, represent the whole of a mother's work and leave plenty of time for spring revelry.

The grub is hatched in about a week; and a strange and paradoxical little creature it is. On its back it has an enormous sugar-loaf hump, the weight of which overbalances it each time that it tries to stand on its legs and walk. At every moment it staggers and falls under the burden of the hunch. The Sacred Beetle's larva showed us long ago a knapsack which was a storehouse of cement to stop up the accidental cracks in the provision-box and protect the food from drying too rapidly. The Onthophagus' grub exaggerates a similar warehouse to the utmost degree; it makes a cone-shaped monument of it, so extravagant and grotesque as to border on caricature. Is it some mad masquerader's joke or a rational deformity which will have its uses later? The future will tell us.

Without saying anything more about it, for lack of words to give a picture of anything so extraordinary, I will refer the reader to the grub of the Oniticellus, which I sketched in an earlier chapter.1 The two hunchbacks are very much alike.

Unable to keep its hump upright, the grub of the Onthophagus lies down on its side in the cell and licks the cream all around it. There is cream everywhere, on the ceiling, on the walls, on the floor. As soon as one spot is thoroughly bared, the consumer moves a little way on with the help of its well-shaped legs; it capsizes again and starts licking again. As the cabin is large and plentifully supplied, the patent-food diet lasts some time.

The fat babies of the Geotrupes, the Copris and the Sacred Beetle finish at one brief sitting the dainty wherewith their narrow lodge is hung, a dainty frugally served and just sufficient to whet the appetite and prepare the stomach for coarser fare; but the Onthophagus' grub, that puny dwarf, has enough to last it for a week and more. The spacious birth-chamber, which is out of all proportion to the nurseling's size, has permitted this wastefulness.

At last the real loaf is attacked. In about a month everything is consumed, except the wall of the sack. And now the splendid part played by the hump stands revealed. Glass tubes, which I had got ready in anticipation, allow me to watch the grub at work. Growing plumper and plumper and more and more humpbacked, it withdraws to one end of the cell, which has become a crumbling ruin. Here it builds a casket in which the transformation will take place. Its materials are the digestive residuum, converted into mortar and heaped up in the hump. The stercoral architect is about to construct a masterpiece of elegance out of its own ordure, held in reserve in that receptacle.

I follow its movements with the magnifying-glass. It curves itself into a loop, closes the circuit of the digestive apparatus, brings its two ends into contact and, with the tip of its mandibles, seizes a pellet of dung evacuated at that moment. This pellet is extracted very neatly and moulded into a brick which is measured most carefully. A slight bend of the creature's neck sets the brick in place. Others follow, laid in the most scrupulously regular courses one above the other. Giving a tap here and there with its palpi, the grub makes sure of the steadiness of the parts, their accurate binding, their orderly arrangement. It turns round in the centre of the work as the edifice rises, even as a mason does when building a turret.

Sometimes the brick that has been laid becomes loose, because the cement has given way. The grub takes it up again with its mandibles, but, before replacing it, coats it with an adhesive moisture. It holds it to its anus, whence a gummy consolidating-extract trickles immediately and almost imperceptibly. The hump supplies the materials; the intestines give, if necessary, the glue that sticks them together.

In this way an attractive house is obtained, ovoid in form, polished as stucco within and adorned on the outside with slightly projecting scales, similar to those on a cedar-cone. Each of these scales is one of the bricks that have been produced from the hump. The casket is not large: a cherry-stone would about represent its dimensions; but it is so accurate, so prettily fashioned that it will bear comparison with the finest products of entomological industry.

The Bull Onthophagus has not a monopoly of this jeweller's art: all, throughout the group, excel in it to the same degree. One of the smallest, the Forked Onthophagus, whose work is hardly larger than a pepper-corn, is as expert as the others in the manufacture of boxes shaped like a cedar-cone. It is a family gift, an invariable gift, despite all differences in size, costume or hornery. The Bison Onitis, the Yellow-footed Oniticellus and certainly many others retire, for the transformation, into a residence similar in architecture to that of the Onthophagi; they too tell us that instincts are independent of structure.

In the first week of July let us complete the destruction of the Bull Onthophagus' cell, already much impaired by the grub, which, after exhausting the contents of its knapsack, has gnawed the inner layer of the walls. The ruins are removed as easily as the husk of a ripe walnut. A sort of shelling process gives us the seed, that is to say, the nymphal casket, which comes out quite neatly, without sticking to its wrapper at any point. Break open the gem. The nymph is there, half-transparent and as it were carved out of crystal. Fortune favours me with a male, who is more interesting because of his frontal armour.

The horns outline a splendid crescent, leaning backwards and resting on the shoulders. They are swollen; they are colourless, like everything that life elaborates in the midst of a generating-fluid; and at their base are the dark ocular specks, not yet capable of sight, but promising to become so. The clypeus is expanding and beginning to stand out. Seen from the front, the head is that of a Bull, with a wide muzzle and enormous horns, copied from those of the Aurochs.

If the artists in the time of the Pharaohs had known the immature Onthophagus, they would certainly have used him for their hieratical images. He is quite as good as the Sacred Beetle and even better from the point of view of those oddities which offer such scope to sacerdotal symbolism. On the front edge of the corselet, a single horn rises, as powerful as the two others and shaped like a cylinder ending in a conical knob. It points forward and is fixed in the middle of the frontal crescent, projecting a little beyond it. The arrangement is gloriously original. The carvers of hieroglyphics would have beheld in it the crescent of Isis wherein dips the edge of the world.

Some other peculiarities complete the nymph's curious appearance. To right and left the abdomen is armed, on either side, with four little horns resembling crystal spikes. Total, eleven pieces in the creature's harness: two on the forehead; one on the thorax; eight on the abdomen. The beast of yore delighted in queer horns: certain reptiles of the geological period stuck a pointed spur on their upper eyelids. The Onthophagus, more greatly daring, sports eight on the sides of his belly, in addition to the spear which he plants upon his back. The frontal horns may be excused: they are fairly common; but what does he propose to do with the others? Nothing at all. They are passing fancies, jewels of early youth; the adult insect will not retain the least trace of them.

The nymph matures. The appendages of the fore-head, at first quite crystalline, now show, when held up to the light, a streak of reddish brown, curved like a bow. This is the real horn taking shape, consistency and colour. The appendage of the corselet and those of the belly, on the other hand, preserve their glassy appearance. They are barren sacks, void of any germ capable of development. The organism produced them in a moment of impulse; now, scornful, or perhaps powerless, it allows its work to wither and become useless.

When the nymph sheds its covering and the delicate tunic of the adult form is rent, these strange horns crumble into fragments, which fall away with the rest of the cast clothing. In the hope of finding at least a trace of the vanished things, the lens vainly explores the bases but lately occupied. There is nothing appreciable left: the nymph is now smooth; the real has given place to the non-existent. Of the accessory panoply so full of promise, absolutely naught remains: everything has vanished into thin air.

The Bull Onthophagus is not the only one endowed with these fleeting appendages, which completely disappear when the nymph sheds its clothes. The other members of the tribe possess similar horny manifestations on their bellies and corselets. One of them, the Spectral Onthophagus, on achieving the perfect state, adorns the front of his corselet with four tiny studs arranged in a semicircle. The two end ones stand alone; the two middle ones are together. These last correspond exactly with the base of the nymph's thoracic horn and might easily be taken for the atrophied remnant of the vanished appendage. We must abandon this idea, however, for the lateral studs, which are more developed than the middle ones, occupy points where the nymph had no horns. In this Onthophagus, as in the others, the nymphal armour is misleading and abortive.

Certain Dung-beetles related to the Onthophagi likewise possess horned nymphs. One of these is the Yellow-footed Oniticellus, the only one whom circumstances have allowed me to examine from this point of view. He wears, in the nymphal stage, a magnificent horn on his corselet and a row of four spikes on each side of his abdomen, as is the rule among the Onthophagi. This all disappears entirely in the adult insect.

It seems likely that, if I had known how to improve the occasion some years ago, when I was successfully rearing the Bison Onitis sent me from Montpellier, I should have perceived the same armour on the nymph's thorax and abdomen. Not having been warned by earlier observations and being anxious also to disturb the pair of strangers as little as possible, I let the opportunity slip.

Let us remark lastly that the Onitis, Oniticellus and Onthophagus genera all three construct for the nymphosis a scaly cabin whose shape suggests the cedar-cone and the fruit of the alder. One may therefore admit, without being too venturesome, that the various builders of similar caskets are all acquainted with the nymphal panoply of a horn on the corselet and a diadem of eight spikes around the abdomen. This is not equivalent to saying that the armour determines the casket or the casket the armour. These curious details go together without influencing each other.

A simple setting forth of the facts is not enough: we should like to see the motive of this horned magnificence. Is it a vague reminiscence of the customs of olden time, when life spent its excess of young sap upon quaint creations, banished to-day from our better-balanced world? Is the Onthophagus the dwarfed representative of an ancient race of horned animals now extinct? Does it give us a faint image of the past?

The surmise rests upon no valid foundation. The Dung-beetle is recent in the general chronology of created beings; he ranks among the last-comers. With him there is no means of going back to the mists of the past, which lends itself to the invention of imaginary precursors. Geological and even lacustrine schists, rich though the latter be in Diptera and Weevils, have hitherto furnished not the slightest relic of the dung-workers. This being so, it is wiser not to claim horned ancestors from the distant past as accounting for those degenerate descendants, the Onthophagi.

Since the past explains nothing, let us turn to the future. If the thoracic horn be not a reminiscence, it may be a promise. It represents a timid attempt, which the ages will harden into a permanent weapon. It lets us assist at the slow and gradual evolution of a new organ; it shows us life in travail of a thing not yet existing on the adult Beetle's corselet, a thing which will exist one day. We catch the genesis of the species in the act; the present teaches us how the future is prepared.

And what does the Beetle propose to do with this object of his ambition, this spear which he hopes by and by to place upon his spine? At any rate as a dazzling piece of masculine finery the thing is already fashionable among the various foreign Scarabs that feed themselves and their grubs on decaying vegetable matter. These giants among the wearers of armoured wing-cases delight in associating their placid corpulence with halberds terrible to gaze upon.

Look at one, Dynastes Hercules by name, a denizen of rotten tree-stumps under the scorching skies of the West Indies. The peaceable colossus well deserves his epithet: he measures three inches long. Of what service can the threatening rapier of the corselet and the toothed lifting-jack of the forehead be to him, unless it be to make him look grand in the presence of his female, herself deprived of these extravagances? Perhaps also they are of use to him in certain operations, even as the trident helps the Minotaurus to crumble his pellets and cart his rubbish. Implements of which we do not know the use always strike us as singular. Having never been intimate with the West-Indian Hercules, I must content myself with suspicions touching the purpose of his fearsome equipment.

Well, one of the subjects in my insect-house would achieve a similar savage finery if he persisted in his attempts. I speak of the Cow Onthophagus (*O. vacca*). His nymph has on its forehead a big horn, one only, bent backward; on its corselet it possesses a similar horn, jutting forward. The two, approaching their tips, look like some kind of pincers. What does the insect lack in order to acquire, on a smaller scale, the eccentric ornament of the West-Indian Scarab? It lacks perseverance. It matures the appendage of the forehead and allows that of the corselet to perish atrophied. It succeeds no better than the Bull Onthophagus in its attempt to grow a pointed stake upon its back; it loses a glorious opportunity of making itself fine for the wedding and terrible in battle.

The others are no more successful. I bring up six different species. All, in the nymphal state, possess the thoracic horn and the eight-pointed ventral coronet; not one benefits by these advantages, which disappear altogether when the adult bursts its wrapping. My near neighbourhood numbers a dozen species of Onthophagi; the world contains some hundreds. All, natives and foreigners, have the same general structure; all most probably possess the dorsal appendage at an early age; and none of them, in spite of the variety of climate, torrid in one place, temperate in another, has succeeded in hardening it into a permanent horn.

Could not the future complete a work whose design is so very clearly traced? We are the more inclined to ask this, because appearances are all in favour of the question. Examine under the magnifying-glass the frontal horns of the Bull Onthophagus in the nymphal state; then with the same scrupulous care look at the spear upon the corselet. At first, there is no difference between them, except for the general configuration. In both cases we find the same glassy aspect, the same sheath swollen with colourless fluid, the same incipient organ plainly marked. A leg in process of formation is not more clearly announced than the horn on the corselet or those on the forehead.

Can time be lacking for the thoracic growth to become organized into a stiff and permanent appendage? The evolution of the nymph is swift; the insect is perfect in a few weeks. Could it not be that, though this brief space suffices to promote the maturity of the horns on the forehead, the thoracic horn requires a longer time to ripen? Let us prolong the nymphal period artificially and give the germ time to develop. It seems to me that a decrease of temperature, moderated and maintained for some weeks, for months if necessary, should be capable of bringing about this result, by delaying the progress of the evolution. Then, with a gentle slowness, favourable to delicate formations, the promised organ will crystallize, so to speak, and become the spear promised by appearances.

The experiment attracted me. I was unable to undertake it for lack of the means whereby to produce a cold, even temperature over a long time. What should I have obtained if my penury had not made me abandon the enterprise? A retarding of the progress of the metamorphosis, but nothing more, apparently. The horn on the corselet would have persisted in its sterility and, sooner or later, would have disappeared.

I have reasons for my conviction. The abode of the Onthophagus engaged on his metamorphosis is not deep down; variations of temperature are easily felt. On the other hand, the seasons are capricious, especially the spring. Under the skies of Provence, the months of May and June, if the mistral lend a hand, have periods when the thermometer drops in such a way as to suggest a return of winter.

To these vicissitudes add the influence of a more northerly climate. The Onthophagi occupy a wide zone of latitude. Those of the north, less favoured by the sun than those of the south, might quite possibly have the date of their transformation postponed by a change in the weather and consequently be subjected to a lower temperature for several weeks. This would spin out the work of evolution and give the thoracic armour time to harden into horn, at rare intervals, as chance may prescribe. Here and there, then, the requisite condition of a moderate or even low temperature at the time of the nymphosis actually exists, without the need of any artificial agency.

Well, what becomes of this surplus time placed at the service of the organic labour? Does the promised horn ripen? Not a bit of it: it withers just as it does under the stimulus of a hot sun. In the records of entomology I find no mention of an Onthophagus carrying a horn upon his corselet. No one would even have suspected the possibility of such an armour, if I had not bruited abroad the strange appearance of the nymph. The influence of climate, therefore, has nothing to do with the matter.

As we go more deeply into it, the question becomes more complicated. The horny appendages of the Onthophagus, the Copris, the Minotaurus and many others are the male's prerogative; the female is without them or wears them only on a reduced and very modest scale. We must look upon these products as personal ornaments rather than as implements of labour. The male makes himself fine for the pairing; but, with the exception of the Minotaurus, who pins down the dry pellet that needs crushing and holds it in position with his trident, I know none that uses his armour as a tool. Horns and prongs on the forehead, crests and crescents on the corselet are the male coquette's jewels and nothing more. The other sex requires no such baits to attract suitors: its femininity is enough; and finery is neglected.

Now here is something to give us food for thought. The nymph of the Onthophagus of the female sex, a nymph with an unarmed forehead, carries on its thorax a vitreous horn as long, as rich in promise as that of the other sex. If this latter excrescence be the design of an incipient ornament, then the former would be so too, in which case the two sexes, both anxious for self-embellishment, would work with equal zeal to grow a horn upon their thorax. We should be witnessing the genesis of a species that would not be really an Onthophagus, but a derivative of the group; we should be beholding the commencement of singularities banished hitherto from among the Dung-beetles, none of whom, of either sex, has thought of planting a spear upon his chine. Stranger still: the female, always the more humbly attired throughout the entomological kingdom, would be vying with the male in her hankering after quaint adornment. An ambition of this sort leaves me incredulous.

We must therefore believe that, if the possibilities of the future should ever produce a Dung-beetle carrying a horn upon his corselet, this upsetter of present customs will not be an Onthophagus who has succeeded in maturing the thoracic appendage of the nymph, but rather an insect resulting from a new model. The creative power throws aside the old moulds and replaces them by others, fashioned with fresh care, in accordance with plans of an inexhaustible variety. Its laboratory is not a peddling rag-fair, where the living assume the cast clothes of the dead: it is a medallist's studio, where each effigy receives the stamp of a special die. Its treasure-house of forms, illimitable in its riches, makes niggardliness impossible: there is no patching up of the old in order to create the new. It breaks every mould once used; it does away with it, without resorting to shabby after-touches.

Then what is the meaning of those horny preparations, which are always blighted before they come to anything? With no great shame I confess that I have not the slightest idea. My reply may not be couched in learned phraseology, but it has one merit, that of absolute sincerity.

1 Chapter XI. of the present volume.—*Translator's Note.*

INDEX

A

Acarus

Ant

Anthidium

Aphis

Aphodius (*see also Aphodius pusillus*)

Aphodius pusillus

Ass

Aurochs

B

Barbier, Jules

Bat

Bee (*see also* Cotton-, Hive-, Mason-, Resin-)

Beetle, *passim*.

Bison (*see* Bison Onitis).

Bison Bubas (*see* Bison Onitis).

Bison Onitis

Black, Adam and Charles

Black-bellied Tarantula (*see* Lycosa).

Blanchard, Émile

Boa Constrictor

Broad-necked Scarab

Bubas (*see also* the varieties below)

Bubas bison (*see* Bison Onitis).

Bubas bubalis

Bull

Bull Onthophagus
Buprestis
Butterfly (*see also* Psyche, White Cabbage Butterfly)
C
Camel
Canary
Capricorn
Carré, Michel
Cat
Century Co.
Cetonia (*see also Cetonia aurata*)
Cetonia aurata (*see* Golden Cetonia).
Chalicodoma
Chamois
Cicada
Clotho Spider
Cockchafer
Copris (*see also* Isis Copris and the varieties below)
Copris hispanus (*see* Spanish Copris).
Copris lunaris (*see* Lunary Copris).
Cotton-bee (*see also* Anthidium)
Cow
Cow Onthophagus
Crane-fly
Cricket
Crocodile
D
Darwin, Charles Robert
Dermestes
Dog, xv-xvi
Donkey (*see* Ass).
Duckling

Dung-beetle, *passim*.
Dynastes Hercules
E
Epeira
Eyed Lizard
F
Fabre, Mlle. Aglaé, the author's daughter
Fabre, Paul, the author's son
Fly
Forked Onthophagus
Franklin, Benjamin
Frisch, Johann Leonhard
G
Gallic Bolboceras
Garden Spider (*see* Epeira).
Geotrupes (*see also* the varieties below)
Geotrupes hypocritus (*see* Mimic Geotrupes).
Geotrupes mutator
Geotrupes stercorarius (*see* Stercoraceous Geotrupes).
Geotrupes sylvaticus
Gnat
Goat
Golden Cetonia
Gorilla
Ground-beetle
Gull (*see* Laughing Gull).
Gymnopleurus (*see also* the varieties below)
Gymnopleurus flagellatus
Gymnopleurus pilularius
H
Half-spotted Scarab
Hedgehog

Hen
Hister
Hive-bee
Horapollo
Horos Apollo (*see* Horapollo).
Horse
Horse-leech
Hydrophilus
I
Ibis
Illiger, Johann Karl Wilhelm
Isis Copris
J
Joseph, the groom
L
Labyrinth Spider
La Fontaine, Jean de
Languedocian Scorpion
Latreille, Pierre André
Laughing Gull
Limnæus
Linnæus, Carl
Lizard (*see* Eyed Lizard).
Locust
Lunary Copris
Lycosa
Lycurgus
M
Macmillan and Co., Ltd.
Mademoiselle Mori, author of
Mantis (*see* Praying Mantis).
Mason-bee (*see* Chalicodoma).

Massé, Victor

Miall, Bernard

Midge

Mimic Geotrupes

Minotaur, Minotaurus (*see Minotaurus typhœus*).

Minotaurus typhœus

Mite (*see* Acarus).

Mole

Monk Onthophagus

Monkey

Montaigne, Michel Eyquem de

Moses

Mule, x-xi

Mulsant, Étienne Marcel

N

Necrophorus

Newt

O

Oniticellus (*see also Oniticellus flavipes*)

Oniticellus flavipes (*see* Yellow-footed Oniticellus).

Onitis (*see also* Bison Onitis)

Onthophagus (*see also* the varieties below)

Onthophagus cænobita (*see* Monk Onthophagus).

Onthophagus fronticornis

Onthophagus furcatus (*see* Forked Onthophagus).

Onthophagus lemur (*see* Spectral Onthophagus).

Onthophagus nuchicornis

Onthophagus Schreberi (*see* Schreber's Onthophagus).

Onthophagus taurus (*see* Bull Onthophagus).

Onthophagus vacca (*see* Cow Onthophagus).

Orus Apollo (*see* Horapollo).

Owl

P

Palæotherium

Pieris (*see* White Cabbage Butterfly).

Pigeon

Pill-rolling Gymnopleurus (*see Gymnopleurus pilularius*).

Pilularius flagellatus

Planorbis

Pock-marked Gymnopleurus (*see Gymnopleurus flagellatus*).

Pock-marked Scarab

Praying Mantis

Proudhon, Pierre Joseph

Psyche

R

Rabelais, François

Ram

Reindeer

Resin-bee (*see* Anthidium).

Rhinoceros

Rodwell, Miss Frances

Rose-chafer (*see* Cetonia).

Rove-beetle (*see* Staphylinus).

S

Sacred Beetle,

Sacred Scarab (*see* Sacred Beetle).

Saperda (*see also* Scalary Saperda)

Scalary Saperda

Scarab (*see also* Sacred Beetle)

Scarabæus (*see* Scarab and the varieties below).

Scarabæus cicatrisosus (*see* Sacred Scarab).

Scarabæus laticollis (*see* Broad-necked Scarab).

Scarabæus sacer (*see* Sacred Beetle).

Scarabæus semipunctatus (*see* Half-spotted Scarab).

Scarred Scarab
Schæffer's Sisyphus
Schreber's Onthophagus
Scolia
Scorpion (*see* Languedocian Scorpion).
Sheep, ,
Silpha
Sisyphus (*see also Sisyphus Schæfferi*)
Sisyphus Schæfferi (*see* Schæffer's Sisyphus).
Snake
Spanish Copris
Sparrow
Spectral Onthophagus
Sphex
Spider (*see also* the several varieties)
Stag
Staphylinus
Starfish
Steer
Stercoraceous Geotrupes
Stickleback
Swallow
T
Teixeira de Mattos, Alexander, *n*
Tick (*see* Acarus).
Titmouse
Toad
Turkey
U
Unwin, T. Fisher
Urquhart, Sir Thomas
V

Vincent de Paul, St.

Virgil

W

Warbler

Wasp (*see also* the several varieties)

Water-snail

Weevil

Wheat-ear

White Cabbage Butterfly

Wren

Y

Yellow-footed Oniticellus